PHYSICS
A LABORATORY MANUAL

OM P. PURI
Clark Atlanta University

PATRICIA J. ZOBER
Ringgold High School

G. PATRICK ZOBER
Yough High School

Pearson
Custom
Publishing

Cover photograph courtesy of PhotoDisc, Inc.

This lab manual is based on:
Experiments in College Physics,
by Om P. Puri, Copyright © 1999, 1995, 1994 by Om P. Puri.
Published by Burgess International Group, Inc.

And excerpts taken from:
Physics 201 Lab Manual, Eighth Edition,
Copyright © 2000, 1998, 1991, 1990, 1981, 1978, 1977, 1976
by the Department of Physics, Texas A & M University.
Published by Pearson Custom Publishing, Inc.

Printed in the United States of America

20 19 18 17 16

Please visit our web site at www.pearsoncustom.com

ISBN 0–13–061146–8

BA 995210

PEARSON CUSTOM PUBLISHING
75 Arlington Street, Suite 300, Boston, MA 02116
A Pearson Education Company

PHYSICS LAB MANUAL

About the Authors

Patricia J. Zober has twenty-five years of experience in teaching AP B and AP C Physics at Ringgold High School in western Pennsylvania. Afer graduation from California State Teachers College, she did her graduate studies at the University of Minnesota.

Patricia is currently a consultant with ETS, is an AP Physics grader, and is a member of the PRAXIS validation committee. For the past two years she has been a member of the Selection Committee for the Pennsylvania Governor's School in Science and serves as an In-Service Presenter for the Pennsylvania Standards in Science Education. She is also a Physics consultant to Holt, Rinehart, and Winston Textbook Publishing Company and to Prentice-Hall Publishing Company. In her spare time, she reads, travels, works crossword puzzles, and is involved with TEAMS and Science Olympiad.

G. Patrick Zober, a native of California, Pennsylvania, has spent most of his professional career teaching physics. After graduation from California State Teachers College, he did his graduate studies at the University of Oklahoma and the University of California at Berkeley.

Besides teaching at Yough High School, he is the district-wide science curriculum coordinator and has served as science department chairperson. He holds a B.S. degree with a dual major in Physics and Mathematics and an M.S. in Theoretical Inorganic Chemistry. During his summers he serves on the staff of both Manhattan College, New York, NY, and Wilkes University, Wilkes Barre, PA, where he teaches Advanced Placement Physics Workshops. In the past he has served as a Physics advisor to the Pennsylvania Department of Education. Presently he is a Physics consultant to Holt, Rinehart, and Winston Textbook Publishing Company and to Prentice-Hall Publishing Company. In his spare time, he writes fiction, enjoys classical music, rides and works on motorcycles, plays with his grandchildren, and finds time to teach an evening class in Engineering Physics at a local community college.

Contents

Physics Lab Policy

1. Study the experiment before you come to the lab and be prepared to ask questions about those parts that you do not understand. Because preparation is essential, you might be given a short quiz covering the basic principles at the beginning of the lab period.

2. Unless otherwise directed by your instructor, there will be one pair of students working at each table. You should take your data together as partners but each student must write the lab report independently. If copying is evident, all students involved will receive severe grade penalties.

3. Each student should have the data sheet initialed by the lab instructor before leaving the lab. The data sheet must include all measurements that you and your partner make in the lab, and it must not be altered later.

4. All students must ensure that when they leave the laboratory, their work area is clean and their experimental apparatus is orderly. The lab instructor will not initial your data sheet until your work area is neat.

5. Be careful not to misuse equipment. If you find that part of your experiment apparatus is faulty or missing, immediately report this to your lab instructor. Do not substitute equipment yourself as it becomes more difficult to keep track of faulty apparatus.

6. All experiments must be performed. A grade of zero for a missed experiment will be recorded unless it is made up. See your instructor for more information.

7. Your instructor will schedule the time each lab report is due. There is a 10% per day penalty for late labs. You are strongly encouraged to write up the lab reports as soon as possible, while the details of the experiment are fresh in your mind.

Introduction

This laboratory course is designed to supplement your physics class and to give you a firsthand knowledge of physics principles and experimental methods through the handling of apparatus designed to demonstrate the meaning and applications of these principles. The objectives of the laboratory course are:

1. To acquire training in scientific methods of observation and recording of data,

2. to acquire techniques in the handling and adjustment of equipment,

3. to become more familiar with the limitations of equipment and uncertainties of measurements,

4. to learn how to take data and develop confidence in your ability to compute reliable answers and determine valid relationships, and

5. to become experienced in the use of graphical representation of data.

The emphasis of this course is in developing appropriate techniques, skills, and scientific attitudes. The accuracy of the numerical results obtained are of secondary importance.

Your laboratory work will be judged on both your performance in the laboratory and on your written report. Procedures for preparing the report are described below.

The equipment and apparatus require careful handling. Report any missing or damaged equipment to your instructor. Your work will not be approved by your instructor unless your equipment has been left in good order.

REPORTING THE EXPERIMENT

One of the most important phases of experimental work is the presentation of findings in an intelligible, convincing form. To conserve the student's time, it is required that the report be elaborate enough merely to be understandable and convincing to one already acquainted with the general nature of the experiment.

(1) THE DATA

Your laboratory report is to be based solely on data obtained experimentally by you and your partner while in the laboratory. Obtaining data consists, essentially, of reading numerical quantities from equipment when it is in predetermined conditions of adjustment and operation. Such readings must never first be jotted down on scratch paper and then be recopied; they must always be recorded *directly* on data sheets and become part of the report. *If any number read directly from equipment is worth writing down anywhere in the laboratory, it must be put directly on a sheet to be kept permanently.* If you make a mistake, draw a line through it and write the other number next to it.

Original data must not be confused with calculated results. By way of illustration, original data on the number of revolutions made by a motor during a certain run consist of the readings of the revolution counter connected to the motor immediately before and immediately after the run. The difference of the two readings, which is the total number of revolutions made during the run, is not a piece of original data but is a calculated result. Original data can be replaced only by performing the experiment again; calculated results can be reproduced any time merely by calculation from the original data. Unlike data, calculations may be carried out initially on scratch paper before they are entered in the permanent report. A well-organized data sheet is often a great aid in locating and correcting an error made while taking data. Data sheets have been provided for your use.

(2) CALCULATIONS

Although it is often preferable not to include other phases of the report on the sheets carrying original data, where advantageous, some calculations may be included on the page with the original data. For instance, averaging of data may be done or intermediate calculated results may appear in columns of the table succeeding the data. Each individual will make his own calculations from the data obtained in partnership. The calculations should be presented neatly in the space provided on the report forms, in sufficient detail that they may be checked readily with a calculator. When more than one calculation using the same equation is made, the results may be listed in a table, accompanied by only a *single* sample calculation worked out in detail. Care must be exercised to carry out all steps of the calculation to a sufficient number of significant figures so as not to jeopardize the results.

(3) GRAPHS

If a graph is to appear in the experiment, it is to be plotted on a separate sheet of *finely divided graph paper*. A title for the graph must appear on the sheet. The independent variable is to be plotted as the abscissa or horizontally, the dependent variable as the ordinate, or vertically. Units are to be chosen in such a way that the graph will occupy a symmetrical spacing on the sheet and the units clearly indicated. A smooth curve is to be drawn averaging the points on the graph, unless specific instruction is given to the contrary. Graphs should always be drawn in pencil. Whenever a slope is to be computed from a graph, it should be done in a corner of the graph that does not interfere with the curve or the data points. Graph paper has been included for your use.

(4) QUESTIONS AND DISCUSSION

The questions at the end of the experiment have been designed to test your knowledge of the experiment. Often they will be worded in a manner that requires you to make a conclusion from your results or to discuss and compare your results in some way. When answering these questions, do so in complete sentences and utilize the physical concepts and formulas you have learned. Be precise and specific, avoid broad and vague answers that say nothing. You are, at this point, demonstrating what you have learned during the course of the experiment and that you have not wasted your time!

(5) ONE LAST THING!!!

Your instructor will inform you of the schedule for the experiments. Therefore, you will know in advance what experiment will be done in your next laboratory session. ALWAYS STUDY THE EXPERIMENT BEFORE COMING TO LAB. Not just because you may be quizzed on it, but mainly because if you don't, you will have a difficult time understanding what you are supposed to do during the laboratory session.

Safety Training

This chapter will assist school district personnel and administrators with guidelines on what must be presented in a professional development program and who should receive it. There are several ways that a school district's safety program can be presented. A well-designed professional development safety program should include information on safety equipment, safety facilities, safety procedures, and first aid. Additional requirements may need to be added according to local school district policy and local safety codes.

In addition to professional development on general safety components, teachers and other district employees must receive instruction on the Texas Hazard Communications Act.

TEXAS HAZARD COMMUNICATIONS ACT (HAZCOM)

The Hazard Communications Act of 1985 was passed during the 69th Legislative Session and became law effective January 1, 1986. The law was later revised during the 73rd Legislative Session and became law effective September 1, 1993. Under section 502.009(b) of the Texas Hazard Communications Act, public schools are to develop, implement, and maintain a written hazard communication program.

WHO SHOULD RECEIVE PROFESSIONAL DEVELOPMENT?

Section 502.004 of the Hazard Communications Act defines an "employee" as a person who may be or may have been exposed to hazardous chemicals in the person's workplace under normal operating conditions or foreseeable emergencies. This includes persons working for this state (school district personnel).

The law requires that all teachers of Prekindergarten through high school and other district personnel must receive training on the Hazard Communications Act prior to working in the area or with the hazardous materials. Teachers new to the profession must receive safety training before they work with or in the area containing the hazardous chemicals, however, district personnel changing assignments only require training on hazardous materials not covered in their initial training and updates. For example, a teacher changing assignments from earth science to chemistry and previously trained on the Hazard Communications Act will require additional training on the hazardous chemicals related to the new teaching assignment.

> "Students are not 'employees' for the purpose of the Texas Hazard Communications Act, Texas Health and Safety Code, Sections 502.001-016. Therefore, the Texas Hazard Communications Act is not applicable to students in their capacity as students except for the requirements of Section 502.004(e)(5)(B) that requires that materials safety data sheets must be maintained by the laboratory and made accessible to students."
> *July 21, 1993 Texas Attorney General ruling, Opinion Number DM-239*

1. A professional development program must include, as appropriate:

   a. understanding and interpreting labels on hazardous chemicals and Material Safety Data Sheets (MSDS) and the relationship between those two methods of hazard communications;

   b. safe handling of hazardous chemicals known to be present in the school district personnel's work area and to which the employee may be exposed;

   c. the proper use of protective equipment and first aid treatment to be used with respect to the hazardous chemicals to which the teacher may be exposed;

   d. general safety instructions on the handling, cleanup procedures, and disposal of hazardous chemicals.

2. Training on hazardous chemicals may be conducted by the categories of the chemicals. The protective equipment and first aid treatment may be accomplished by categories of hazardous chemicals as well.

3. Teachers and other school district personnel must receive additional training when the potential for exposure to hazardous chemicals in the work area increases significantly or when the school district receives new and significant information concerning the hazards of a chemical in the employee's work area.

4. The school district shall provide training to a new or newly assigned teacher, administrator, or other school district personnel before the individual works with or in an area containing a hazardous chemical.

5. The school district shall keep a written hazard communications program and a record of each training session given to school district personnel, including the date, a roster of the employees who attended, the subjects covered in the training session, and the names of the instructors. Those records shall be maintained for at least 5 years by the school district. The Texas Department of Health will have access to those records and may interview teachers during compliance inspections.

HAZCOM GUIDELINES FOR SCHOOL DISTRICTS

The Texas Department of Health recommends the following steps as a guide for the development of a district-wide safety-training program.

1. Create a list of all district personnel that require safety training.

2. Determine the appropriate level of training for different job classifications based on the number and type of chemicals, chemical categories used, and the duration and frequency of use.

3. Designate a person(s) responsible for conducting the safety training.

4. Determine the format of the safety program to include visuals, classroom instruction, hands-on instruction, materials required.

5. Elements of the training program should include but should not be limited to:

- Texas Hazard Communications Act—purpose and application,
- use, location, and interpretation of Materials Safety Data Sheets (MSDS),
- location, health effects, and safe handling of hazardous chemicals present in the work area,
- proper use of protective equipment—safety goggles, lab aprons, safety gloves, etc.,
- first aid treatment with respect to hazardous chemical exposure,
- safety instructions on the labeling, handling, cleanup, and disposal of hazardous chemicals,
- the employee rights under the Texas Hazard Communications Act.

6. Describe the procedures for training new or newly assigned employees where hazardous chemicals may be found.

7. Describe the procedures for providing periodic update safety training.

8. Describe the school district's procedures for responding to an emergency situation involving hazardous chemicals.

9. Establish a procedure for maintaining records of training sessions that include:

- dates of the training sessions
- a list of district personnel trained
- topics covered in the safety session
- name of the instructor(s)
- retention of this information for at least 5 years

The school district has the responsibility to obtain an MSDS for each hazardous chemical used in the schools. Copies of the MSDS are to be maintained on each campus readily available to teachers and other district personnel upon request. Generic MSDS that comply with OSHA standards are acceptable in lieu of the manufacturer's MSDS.

For further information on the requirements of a HAZCOM training program, contact:

Texas Department of Health
Hazard Communications Branch
1100 West 49th Street
Austin, Texas 78756
(512) 834-6603

SAFETY TRAINING FOR STUDENTS

The science laboratory is a place of discovery and investigation. One of the first things students discover is that learning in a laboratory is an exciting experience. The laboratory can also be a dangerous place to work if proper safety rules are not established and followed. To prepare students for a successful year in science, the teachers should develop safety rules that incorporate the following safety information.

PERSONAL PROTECTIVE EQUIPMENT

1. Many materials in the laboratory cause eye injury. Protect yourself from possible injury by wearing the splash-proof safety goggles provided in the laboratory. In Texas schools, state law requires that safety goggles be worn in all situations where the possibility of injury to the eye is present. This includes working with chemicals, heating materials, and using certain kinds of equipment.

2. Wear laboratory aprons or coats when working with chemicals or heated substances.

3. Wear protective gloves when handling hazardous chemicals and materials.

PROPER DRESS

1. Wear long-sleeved blouses and shirts. Regular length slacks or denim jeans provide good protection for your legs. Shorts will not protect the legs and are not appropriate when working in a laboratory.

2. Tie back long hair to prevent it from coming into contact with chemicals or an open flame.

3. Wear shoes without open ends. Sandals will not protect the feet from spills or other injuries and should never be worn in a laboratory.

4. Remove or tie back any article of clothing or jewelry that hangs down from the body and might come into contact with chemicals or open flames.

GENERAL LABORATORY RULES

1. Read all directions for doing a laboratory investigation before beginning. Be alert in the laboratory and listen for the teacher's directions. Ask questions if you do not understand any part of the investigation.

2. Never perform activities that are not authorized by the teacher.

3. Do not handle equipment without specific permission.

4. Take extra precautions when handling chemicals. Never pour chemicals or other substances into the sink or trash container. If a chemical spill occurs, notify the teacher immediately.

5. Never eat or drink in the laboratory. Never drink from a beaker or other container used in the laboratory.

6. There should never be loud talking or playing in the laboratory.

7. Handle cutting instruments carefully. Never cut materials toward you—use a cutting motion away from yourself.

8. When you have completed the investigation, clean up your work area and return equipment and supplies to their proper place.

9. Wash your hands with soap and warm water after every investigation.

10. Turn off all burners before leaving the laboratory.

11. Know the location and use of all safety equipment (fire extinguishers, eye/face wash station, safety shower, fire blankets, chemical spill kits).

12. Never work in the laboratory alone or without permission.

13. Do not enter supply or storage rooms without a teacher present or without the teacher's permission.

FIRST-AID PROCEDURES

1. Report all accidents to your teacher immediately.

2. Learn what to do in case of an accident (such as an acid spilling on the body, materials entering the eye, and cuts or burns).

- When chemicals splash onto the body, rush to the safety shower, pull the handle, and remain in the shower for at least 15 minutes.
- If materials enter your eye, rush to the eye/face wash station and flush the eyes with a continuous stream of water for at least 15 minutes. Hold your eyelids open with your fingers, or get assistance from your teacher.
- Report minor cuts or burns to the teacher, so that he or she can administer first aid in the laboratory.

3. Be aware of the location of the first-aid kit, but allow the nurse to administer first aid to an injured student.

USE FIRE SAFELY

1. Do not use an open flame without first putting on safety goggles.

2. Know how to light and regulate the flame on a burner.

3. Never leave an open flame unattended. When the burner is not being used, turn it off.

4. Keep your area clean and free from clutter.

5. Do not reach across an open flame.

6. Always point the open end of a test tube away from others when heating liquids. Some chemicals can boil out of the test tube violently and unexpectedly when being heated.

7. Never heat chemicals in a closed container such as a corked test tube. The expanding gas inside will cause the test tube to explode or turn the stopper into a projectile with considerable force.

8. Do not pick up a container that has been heated or hand a heated container to someone. Hold the back of your hand near the container and check for heat. If you can feel heat, use a mitten or tongs to pick up the container.

Use Chemicals Safely

1. Never touch, taste, or smell any chemical that you do not know is harmless. Many chemicals are toxic. If you are instructed to smell fumes during an investigation, do so by gently waving your hand over the container so that the fumes are brought to you. Do not bring the container to your nose. Do not inhale the fumes directly from the container, as they may be concentrated and cause you injury.

2. Use only chemicals that are listed in the investigation, and do not substitute other chemicals for the ones listed.

3. Notify the teacher immediately if chemicals have been spilled.

4. Dispose of the chemicals properly as directed by the teacher. Do not pour them into the sink or trash container.

5. Use extra precautions with acids and bases. Always pour acid into water. Do not pour water into acids.

6. Remember to wash any acid or base from your skin immediately and notify the teacher.

7. Use a pipette bulb. Never pipette liquids using your mouth.

8. Read the labels twice before using a chemical.

9. Do not pour extra chemicals back into the original container. This causes contamination of the chemical and may cause incorrect results to occur in future investigations.

10. Never use the same spatula to remove chemicals from two different containers. Each container should have its own spatula.

11. When removing a stopper from a bottle, do not lay it on the lab table, but place the stopper between two fingers and hold the bottle so that the label is in the palm of your hand. Both the bottle and the stopper should be held in one hand.

12. Replace all stoppers and caps on the correct bottles after you have finished using them.

Use Glassware Safely

1. Never force glass tubing into a rubber stopper. Use a lubricant and a turning motion on the glass tubing when inserting it into a rubber stopper or rubber tubing.

2. When heating glassware, use a wire or ceramic screen to protect the glassware from the flame.

3. After cutting glass tubing, always fire polish the ends to remove any sharp edges.

4. Never use broken or chipped glassware. If glassware breaks, notify your teacher and properly dispose of it in a broken glassware container.

5. Never eat or drink from laboratory glassware.

6. Clean glassware thoroughly before returning it to storage.

USE ELECTRICAL EQUIPMENT SAFELY

1. Be careful not to shock yourself or another person.

2. Turn off all power sources when setting up circuits or repairing equipment.

3. Do not use metal articles such as rulers, metal pencils or writing pens; do not wear rings, metal watchbands, or bracelets when working with electrical equipment.

4. When disconnecting electrical equipment, pull from the plug and not the wire.

5. Use caution when handling electrical equipment that has been in use. The equipment may be warm or hot from being used.

6. Never connect, disconnect, or operate a piece of electrical equipment with wet hands or while standing on a wet floor.

OTHER PRECAUTIONS

1. Do not use hair spray, hair mousse, or other flammable hair products during or just before laboratory work where an open flame is used. These products may contain highly flammable chemicals and ignite easily.

2. Synthetic fingernails are also highly flammable and should not be worn in the laboratory.

PROFESSIONAL DEVELOPMENT

Teachers should maintain a record of professional development they have received on safety. Using the Professional Development Profile and working with district administrators, teachers can identify the areas of safety they need to learn more about to provide a safe learning environment for their students. Science coordinators and supervisors can collect this information to provide districtwide staff development for their teachers.

PROFESSIONAL DEVELOPMENT PROFILE

EQUIPMENT

Telephone
- ☐ emergency numbers
- ☐ locations
- ☐ portable communications

Fire Extinguishers
- ☐ types and uses
- ☐ location

Public Address System
- ☐ location
- ☐ emergency use

Eye Protection Devices
- ☐ law requirements
- ☐ types of protection
- ☐ purpose
- ☐ sanitation and storage

Fire Blankets
- ☐ purpose
- ☐ location

Spill Control Kit
- ☐ types
- ☐ purpose
- ☐ proper use
- ☐ location
- ☐ disposal

FACILITIES

Corrosive Materials Cabinet
- ☐ purpose
- ☐ location
- ☐ chemical storage
- ☐ ventilation

Broken Glass Containers
- ☐ purpose
- ☐ location
- ☐ proper disposal

Electrical Safety
- ☐ circuit breaker box
- ☐ electrical outlets
- ☐ extension cords
- ☐ location of outlets
- ☐ hazards

Emergency Showers
- ☐ law requirements
- ☐ location
- ☐ proper use
- ☐ purpose
- ☐ routine tests

Eye/Face Wash Stations
- ☐ law requirements
- ☐ water temperature
- ☐ water pressure
- ☐ types and purpose

Flammable Materials Cabinet
- ☐ purpose
- ☐ location
- ☐ chemical storage

Master Utility Controls
- ☐ purpose
- ☐ types of controls
- ☐ location
- ☐ maintenance
- ☐ security

Chemical Safety (HAZCOM)
- ☐ types of chemicals
- ☐ ventilation
- ☐ shelving
- ☐ chemical storage
- ☐ MSDS

Forced Air Ventilation
- ☐ law requirements
- ☐ purpose
- ☐ uses
- ☐ locations

Safety Signs
- ☐ types
- ☐ purpose
- ☐ locations

Compressed Gas Cylinders
- ☐ types
- ☐ pressure hazards
- ☐ transporting
- ☐ security

Fume Hoods
- ☐ requirements
- ☐ location
- ☐ purpose and use

Emergency Exhaust Fan
- ☐ purpose and use

PROCEDURES

Fire Drill Procedures
- ☐ fire drill rules
- ☐ posting evacuation routes

Safety Contract
- ☐ student contract
- ☐ purpose and use

Emergency Procedures
- ☐ developing procedures
- ☐ what to do in an emergency
- ☐ when and how to call for assistance
- ☐ field investigations

First-Aid Procedures
- ☐ handling cuts, burns, and minor injuries
- ☐ reporting and keeping records
- ☐ when to call for assistance
- ☐ who to call for assistance
- ☐ CPR training
- ☐ abdominal thrust
- ☐ field investigations

EXAMPLES OF COMMON SAFETY SYMBOLS

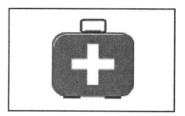

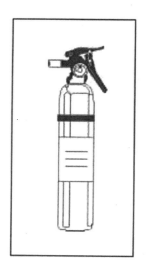

Graphical Analysis

THEORY

Graphs are useful in representing relationships existing between variables in a visual form. They are used extensively by scientists as they search for relationships because they clearly reveal relationships that may be obscured by large tables of data and allow one to quickly see the relationship between two quantities. For instance, a straight-line relationship indicates that the variables are directly and linearly proportional; a hyperbolic graph indicates that one variable increases while the other decreases; hence the variables are inversely proportional. This laboratory exercise will give you some of the procedures that should be followed in constructing graphs and will familiarize you with some of the simpler relations shown by graphs.

It is often said that we are living in an age of information, or that we are faced with an "information explosion". This is no doubt true, and a substantial fraction of this information is in the form of tables of numbers. An economist may have the steel production per month for the last 10 years, or a historian may have the population of Florida each year for the last 100 years in the form of a list of numbers. The examples are endless, but the problems are universally the same: How does one extract meaningful information such as trends and relationships from such data? One method of approaching this problem is to use a graph to show how one quantity changes with respect to another. A philosopher many centuries ago said that a picture is worth a thousand words, so are graphs. A graph is a picture representation of ordered pairs of numbers. Graphs are used extensively by physicists as they search for relationships. Graphs reveal relationships and they are one of the least involved methods of determining these relationships.

COORDINATES

Draw a horizontal and a vertical line that intersect at right angles at a point in the lower left-hand corner of a sheet of graph paper. We will call this framework a frame-of-reference. See Figure 1.1. These lines of the frame-of-reference are called coordinate axis and should be made as large as possible to fit the sheet of graph paper. The vertical axis is usually designated as the y-axis or the *ordinate*. The horizontal axis is designated as the x-axis or the *abscissa*. The point where the x and the y-axis meet is the *origin* of the frame-of-reference. Usually this point represents zero for both axes.

Purpose

To become familiar with the use of graphs in the analysis of experimental data.

Apparatus

Graph paper, straightedge ruler, and French curve.

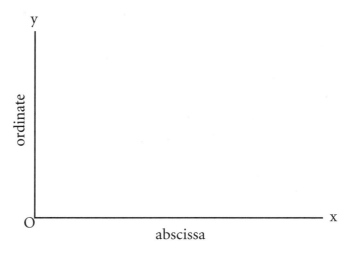

Figure 1.1

VARIABLES

The term variable refers to a "quantity that may assume any one of a specified set of values". When studying an experimental system of a "cause and effect" nature, one is usually concerned with two such quantities (variables). The basic procedure followed is to vary one condition (the cause) and observe corresponding changes in another (the effect). In order that a graph is easily and accurately interpreted, the INDEPENDENT VARIABLE (the cause) is plotted on the x-axis or the abscissa, and the DEPENDENT VARIABLE (the effect) is plotted on the y-axis or the ordinate.

SCALES

The size of the scale for each axis is chosen with regard to the range of numbers to be plotted. Generally, the curve should occupy as much of the graph as possible.

The range of the values of the dependent variable (y-axis) should be evaluated. A scale is chosen so that the main divisions on the graph paper are easily subdivided, and the entire range of data is included. Values such as 1, 2, 5, 10, or 100 are most successful as subdivisions. Values such as 3, 7, 9, or 13 make reading a graph very difficult and should be avoided. The scale should be arranged so that each main division (or isolated square) on the graph paper has the same numerical value, and so that the values increase additively as they move away from the origin. The same procedure is used for the scaling of the x-axis; however, the x and y-axis are independent of one another and need not be identical. See Figure 1.2.

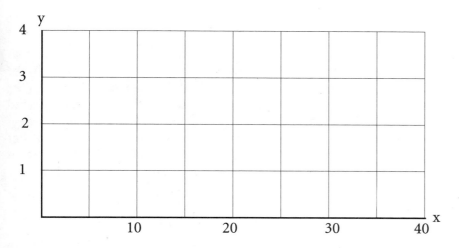

Figure 1.2

PLOTTING

Each point on a graph can be located using two numbers—the value of the x-coordinate, and the value of the y-coordinate. An example of this would be the point (4,3). See Figure 1.3. Generally, any point on the graph can be specified by the notation (x,y).

The location of each point plotted that can be located from experimental data is designated by a dot from a pencil.

The plotted data points will reveal the relationship that exists between the x and y variables. To illustrate this relationship pictorially, a smooth curve should be drawn to follow the general pattern indicated by the points. When plotting experimental data, it is probable that all the points will not lie directly on the curve. In a case such as this, a smooth curve should be drawn through the points, being careful to follow the general trend, to give an average representation as in Figure 1.4.

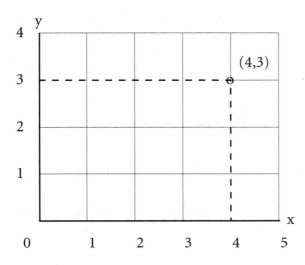

Figure 1.3

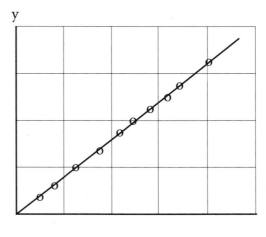

Figure 1.4

LABELING

The quantity being plotted along each axis should be clearly stated on that axis. Whenever the scale along either axis has units associated with it, the units should be clearly stated with the scale along the axis. A title should be placed at the top of each graph stating what quantities are being plotted against one another. State the title as dependent variable vs. the independent variable. It is usually best to write the title across the top of the graph after the points have been plotted so that it will not interfere with the visibility of the curve. See Figure 1.5 as an example.

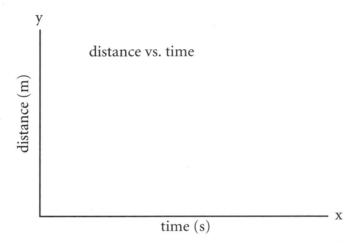

Figure 1.5

The simplest kind of relationship between two variables is a straight-line, and straight lines are represented by the slope-intercept equation:

$$y = mx + b \qquad\qquad (1)$$

If the variable x is assigned the value x = 0, then $y = m(0) + b$, and y = b. That is, b is the value of y where the curve crossed the y-axis, and for this reason is called the *y-intercept*. The constant m is called the *slope* or the inclination of the line. By definition, the slope of the straight line is the ratio by which y changes with respect to x.

$$m = slope = \frac{change\ in\ y}{change\ in\ x} \qquad\qquad (2)$$

The slope can be calculated by choosing two points on the line. To distinguish between the coordinates of two arbitrary points, the coordinates of point 1 will have a subscript 1, and the coordinates of point 2 will have a subscript 2.

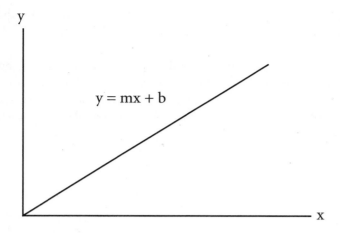

Figure 1.6

To find the change in the y-coordinate, we subtract, $y_2 - y_1$, which is de-noted by Δy (Δ is the Greek letter "delta", and means "the change in"). To find the change in the x-coordinate, we subtract, $x_2 - x_1$, which is defined as Δx.

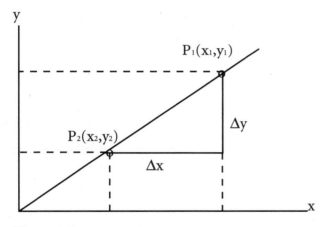

Figure 1.7

Now, the slope becomes:

$$m = slope = \frac{\Delta y}{\Delta x} = \frac{y_2 - y_1}{x_2 - x_1} \qquad (2a)$$

For any straight line, this value will be a constant, regardless of the points chosen for the calculation.

Perhaps you have been driving in the mountains and have seen road signs giving the slope of the road. These signs gave the increase in altitude for a given horizontal distance of forward travel. This turns out to be an excellent method for describing the "steepness" of grade of a road, and for that reason this ratio is called the *slope*.

The straight-line graph is not the only type encountered in the analysis of data. These cases must all be handled individually, and we shall do one more example here to illustrate the possibilities. Suppose that we have an equation $y = Ax^2$, where A is a constant. The graph of this equation is a curve called a parabola, Figure 1.8.

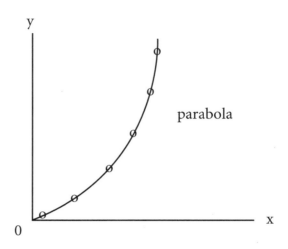

Figure 1.8

Suppose you have an equation $y = \dfrac{k}{x}$ or, $xy = k$ where k is a constant. The graph of this equation is a hyperbola, Figure 1.9. This is another curve you will be plotting in the laboratory.

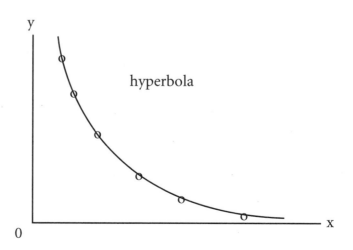

Figure 1.9

LEARNING OBJECTIVES

After completing this experiment you should be able to do the following:

1. Define the word graph.
2. Explain the important properties of a graph.
3. Plot a graph from the given data.
4. Determine the slope of the plotted data points.
5. State the physical interpretations of the slope.

PROCEDURE

Plot the following graphs from the data presented below. Answer the questions after you have plotted the graphs.

GRAPH I. A graph of the money spent (y-axis) by a storekeeper for sugar as a function of sugar in pounds (x-axis) he buys:

Money Spent (dollars)	*0*	*2*	*4*	*8*	*16*	*24*	*32*	*36*	*?*
Sugar Bought (pounds)	*0*	*50*	*100*	*200*	*400*	*600*	*800*	*900*	*1000*

PRACTICE QUESTIONS

1. Draw a graph using the following data points:

x = 0	y = 0	
x = 1	y = 1.1	
x = 2	y = 3.8	
x = 3	y = 8.7	
x = 4	y = 16.5	y is displacement in cm
x = 5	y = 25.0	x is time in seconds (s)

2. Draw a graph using the following data points:

x = 21	y = 400	
x = 38	y = 200	
x = 82	y = 100	y is volume (V) of a gas in mL

x = 155	y = 50	x is pressure (P) in cm of mercury
x = 320	y = 25	

3. Graph the data in practice questions 2 this time by plotting y vs. $\frac{1}{x}$. What does this indicate?

4. Determine the mathematical relationship between the variables in each of the above cases.

5. Plot a graph of the equation $y = x^2$. What type of mathematical relationship is there between the variables?

6. Which of the points in the two practice questions have the greatest error? Why do you think so?

GRAPH II.   A lecturer is talking to a class of 72 students in a lecture period that is 50 minutes long. The lecturer is very boring, and the students steadily fall asleep as time goes on. From the data below plot a graph of the number of students asleep as a function of time.

No. of Sleeping Students (N)	0	8	18	28	36	54	62	67	72
Time in Minutes (min)	0	5	10	15	20	30	35	40	50

GRAPH III.   In an experiment performed at a drag strip, a go-cart's distance from the starting line was recorded at intervals of 10 seconds (s).

Distance (ft)	0	80	320	720	1280	2000
Time (s)	0	10	20	30	40	50

(a) Plot a graph of distance as a function of time (distance vs. time).

(b) Plot a graph of distance as a function of time squared (distance vs. t^2).

GRAPH IV.   Data was obtained by observing the temperature of a beaker of hot oil as it cooled. Plot a graph of temperature vs. time. Analyze this graph.

Temperature (°F)	200	121	77	52	38	30

Time (min)	0	8	16	24	32	40

GRAPH V.   During a physics experiment a student varied the current (I) in amperes (A) passing through an electrical resistor. The student found that as the current was increased, the voltage drop (V) across the resistor also increased. Plot the graph voltage drop vs. current (V vs. I).

Voltage drop (in volts, V)	0	6.3	12.6	16.0	31.6	50.6	69.5	84.0
Current (in amperes, A)	0	0.4	0.8	1.2	2.0	3.2	4.4	5.6

QUESTIONS

1. How might you determine slope(s) for Graph IV?

2. If the price of sugar remains the same and if there is available as much sugar as may be needed, can Graph I predict the cost of any amount of sugar the storekeeper may wish to buy?

3. What kind relationship does Graph I represent?

4. Of the two graphs, III(a) and III(b), which is easier to analyze and why?

5. What are the units of the slope of Graph III(b)?

6. What is the shape of Graph IV? What relationship is suggested? When will the oil have a temperature of 100°F? What is the temperature of the oil 20 minutes after cooling began?

7. Analyze Graph V. Determine the slope of the curve. Find the intercept and write the equation of the curve. Use your equation and calculate the voltage drop for a current of 1.0 A. Use your graph and find the voltage drop for a current of 1.0 A. How do these values compare? Use your graph and find the current for a voltage of 60.0 volts.

Measurements

THEORY

When a physical quantity is measured, the result of the measurement is expressed by means of a number that represents its numerical size and a unit in terms of which the quantity is measured. The *fundamental units* are the units in which the fundamental quantities of length, mass, and time are measured. These fundamental quantities can be expressed in either the English system using the foot (ft), pound (lb), and second (s) or the SI system using the meter (m), kilogram (kg), and second (s). The units that are derived from the fundamental units on the basis of established physical relationships or laws are called *derived units*.

To make an accurate determination of a physical quantity such as the gravitational constant, the coefficient of expansion, or the length of an object, many readings must be taken and averaged. The agreement of these values with one another is a measure of the accuracy with which the quantity has been determined. In elementary laboratory work, time does not permit intensive research, so results vary from each other and from handbook values. An essential part of reporting an experiment is the indication of this variation or error and a statement of possible sources of error.

The *error* is the difference between the expected result (or handbook value) and the experimental result. For measurements such as those of length where there is no expected value the probable error may be computed by estimating the error involved in each measuring process. The probable error should never be expressed with more than one significant figure, and the experimental value should never be expressed more accurately than indicated by the probable error.

The percent error is defined as the error, the absolute value of the difference between the expected value and the experimental value, divided by the expected value and multiplied by 100%. Or

$$\% \text{ error} = \frac{|\text{error}|}{\text{expected value}} \times 100\% = \frac{|\text{expected value} - \text{experimental value}|}{\text{expected value}} \times 100\%$$

As an example let us say that an experimental value is determined to be 4.34 and the handbook value (expected value) is 4.32, the error is

$$\text{error} = |4.32 - 4.34| = 0.02$$

Source: Puri
Modified by Zober and Zober

Purpose

An integral part of any laboratory procedure is the ability to make accurate measurements. In this experiment, you are asked to investigate the process of measurement and to determine the accuracy of various measuring instruments. In addition, you will be introduced to the measurement of the three fundamental quantities—length, mass, and time.

Apparatus

Card, meterstick, English-SI ruler, Vernier caliper, micrometer, set of density metal cylinders, balance and masses, several wooden blocks of various sizes, and several small spheres.

And the % error is

$$\% \text{ error} = \frac{|\text{error}|}{\text{expected value}} \times 100\% = \frac{0.02}{4.32} \times 100\% = 0.463\%$$

Which should be rounded to 0.5%.

When many readings are taken of the same quantity, the average deviation of the readings from the mean is a good estimate of the probable error in the experiment. For example, suppose that the length of a sample is measured with the following results:

Reading	Length (cm)	Absolute Deviation from the Mean
1	3.54	0.01
2	3.52	0.01
3	3.53	0.00
4	3.55	0.02
5	3.51	0.02
sum	17.65	0.06

$$\text{Mean value for the length} = \frac{17.65}{5} = 3.53$$

The average deviation is $\frac{0.06}{5} = 0.012 = 0.01$, keeping only one significant figure. This value of 0.01 is the probable error in the determination of the length of the object, and should be reported as:

$$\text{Length} = 3.53 \text{ cm} \pm 0.01 \text{ cm}$$

This means that any future readings will most likely lie between 3.52 and 3.54 cm.

In making measurements, figures obtained from the measuring instruments are called significant figures. In a measured quantity, all figures are considered significant except those used to locate the decimal point. For example, you are asked to measure the width of a small study table. You report an answer of 1.65 m. In this case all three figures are significant. Suppose you are asked to calculate the distance between your home and school and your answer is 3 200 m. In this case, only the 3 and the 2 are significant. Suppose further that it is necessary for you to measure the length of your laboratory notebook using a stick calibrated in centimeters only. It measures a little longer than 28 cm but less than 29 cm and seems to be about 5 tenths of the way from 28 to 29, or 28.5 cm long. Then the same book is measured with a ruler calibrated in centimeters and tenths of centimeters. The new measurement is 28.45 cm. The first measurement (28.5 cm) has three significant figures; the second (28.45 cm) has four significant figures. The difference between these two measurements is the degree of precision with which they have been made.

In this experiment we will make measurements on a set of blocks and it will be important to be as accurate as possible. We will first measure a block in inches and then in cgs-metric unit of the centimeter. From the information, called *data,* that we gather we will determine an experimental conversion factor.

In physics we say that one measurement is no measurement. If you measure an object and commit a measuring error, you have no way of knowing that your work is incorrect. Making a second and third measurement makes a measuring error unlikely. For this reason we will make a set of three measurements or determinations or trials in most of our experimental work. In this experiment we will make three sets of measurements, or, as we say, three trials.

Materials have two sets of properties, chemical and physical. Chemical properties deal with how substances react chemically. Does it burn? Will it support combustion? How does it react with acids or bases? Physical properties deal with properties we usually determine through our senses. What is the color of the substance? What is its odor? What is its taste? What is the melting point? What is the boiling point? What is the phase under normal conditions? There are many others we will learn about in our study of physics.

One of the more important of the physical properties is density. In dealing with the SI system we refer to this property as *mass density*. Simply stated, mass density, ρ, is defined as the mass of a material divided by its volume, or, mathematically

$$\rho = \frac{m}{V} \tag{1}$$

In dealing with small objects it is convenient to use the cgs-metric where m is mass in grams, g, V is the volume in cm³, and ρ is the mass density in $\frac{g}{cm^3}$.

To calculate the volume of a cylinder we use the formula

$$V = \pi R^2 L \tag{2}$$

Where L is length of the cylinder and R is radius.

The volume of a sphere is given by

$$V = \frac{4}{3}\pi R^3 \tag{3}$$

After completing the experiment you should be able to do the following:

1. Increase the precision of your measurements by the correct use of the Vernier caliper and the micrometer.

2. Explain the difference between the fixed scale and the movable scale of the Vernier caliper.

3. Calculate the volume and the density of an object.

4. Be able to express you answer in significant figures.

5. In determining the volume of a cylinder you should be able to explain what dimension needs to be the most "precise".

6. Be able to calculate absolute error and percent error.

PROCEDURE

PART A.

1. Using a meterstick, take 10 measurements, in centimeters, of the length of a card issued to you. Determine the mean value, average deviation, and the % deviation. In the same way, measure the width of the card. From these measurements calculate the area of the card and indicate the reliability of your result quantitatively.

2. Repeat the length measurement described above, this time making the measurements in inches. From the two measurements of length, calculate the ratio $\frac{cm}{in}$. Determine the reliability of the result. Calculate the % error in your result, assuming that the correct value of the ratio is $2.540 \frac{cm}{in}$.

PART B.

3. Choose a block. This block is your first choice and will be treated as such in future reference.

4. Using the English side of the ruler, carefully and as accurately as possible, measure the dimensions of the block. Convert any fractional value into a decimal. Record these measurements in your data. Do a second and a third trial on the block and record.

5. Using the metric side of the ruler, repeat the above procedure measuring the block in centimeters and record these dimensions in your data.

6. Find the average length, width, and height of the block for both systems. Use these average values and calculate the volume of the block in cubic centimeters and cubic inches.

7. Divide the average volume of the block in cubic centimeters by the volume in cubic inches. This value is your experimental conversion factor for cubic centimeters and cubic inches. The accepted value is $16.39 \frac{cm^3}{in^3}$. How does this value compare with your experimental value? Find the error and % error.

8. Take a second block and make the same measurements and calculations you did for the first block. Record these values.

PART C.

9. Pick one of the metal cylinders. After instruction of the use of the Vernier caliper, measure the length and diameter of the cylinder. Make 3 trials and record the data.

10. Use the average radius and length and calculate the volume of the cylinder. Record.

11. Mass the cylinder on a balance. Record your mass in grams.

12. Calculate the mass density of the cylinder, R. Compare your experimental mass density to accepted values in the density table in the appendix of your lab manual.

13. Repeat the above procedures for a second cylinder.

PART D.

14. After instruction on the use of the micrometer, measure the diameter of one of the spheres.

15. Mass the sphere and record this mass.

16. Calculate the mass density of the sphere. Compare your experimental mass density to accepted values in the density table in the appendix of your lab manual.

17. Repeat the above procedures with a second sphere.

QUESTIONS

1. In measuring the dimensions of a cylinder for calculating the volume, which dimension needs to be more precise?

2. If you make a 1% error in the measurement of either the diameter or the length of a cylinder, what is the error in the volume?

3. How is the surface area of a sphere related to its volume?

4. Explain how you would measure the density of an irregular solid.

5. Can you accurately measure the volume of a material that floats? How would you measure the volume?

Measurements

Name: _____   Date: _____

PART A.

Trial	Length L	Width W	Length L	Width W
No.	cm	cm	in	in
1				
2				
3				
4				
5				
6				
7				
8				
9				
10				

Length:

Mean value _____ cm   Mean value _____ in

Average deviation _____ cm   Average deviation _____ in

% Deviation _____ %   % Deviation _____ %

Width:

Mean value _____ cm   Mean value _____ in

Average deviation _____ cm   Average deviation _____ in

% Deviation _____ %   % Deviation _____ %

Area:

Area _____ cm^2 Area _____ in^2

Experimental conversion factor _____ $\dfrac{cm}{in}$

Accepted value 2.540 $\dfrac{cm}{in}$

Error _____ $\dfrac{cm}{in}$

% Error _____ %

Part B.

Block 1

Trial No.	Length L cm	Width W cm	Height H cm	Length L in	Width W in	Height H in
1						
2						
3						

Average volume _____ cm³

Average volume _____ in³

Experimental conversion factor _____ $\dfrac{cm^3}{in^3}$

Accepted value 16.39 $\dfrac{cm^3}{in^3}$

Error _____ $\dfrac{cm^3}{in^3}$

% Error _____ %

BLOCK 2

Trial	Length L	Width W	Height H	Length L	Width W	Height H
No.	cm	cm	cm	in	in	in
1						
2						
3						

Average volume _____ cm^3

Average volume _____ in^3

Experimental conversion factor _____ $\dfrac{cm^3}{in^3}$

Accepted value 16.39 $\dfrac{cm^3}{in^3}$

Error _____ $\dfrac{cm^3}{in^3}$

% Error _____ %

PART C.

CYLINDER 1   MATERIAL _____

Trial	Length L	Diameter D	Radius R
No.	cm	cm	cm
1			
2			
3			

Volume _____ cm^3

Mass _____ g

Experimental mass density _____ $\dfrac{g}{cm^3}$

Accepted mass density _____ $\dfrac{g}{cm^3}$

Error _____ $\dfrac{g}{cm^3}$

% Error _____ %

CYLINDER 2   MATERIAL _____

| Trial | Length L | Diameter D | Radius R |
No.	cm	cm	cm
1			
2			
3			

Volume _____ cm^3

Mass _____ g

Experimental mass density _____ $\dfrac{g}{cm^3}$

Accepted mass density _____ $\dfrac{g}{cm^3}$

Error _____ $\dfrac{g}{cm^3}$

% Error _____ %

PART D.

SPHERE 1   MATERIAL _____

Trial	Length L	Diameter D	Radius R
No.	cm	cm	cm
1			
2			
3			

Volume _____ cm^3

Mass _____ g

Experimental mass density _____ $\dfrac{g}{cm^3}$

Accepted mass density _____ $\dfrac{g}{cm^3}$

Error _____ $\dfrac{g}{cm^3}$

% Error _____ %

SPHERE 2   MATERIAL _____

Trial No.	Length L cm	Diameter D cm	Radius R cm
1			
2			
3			

Volume _____ cm^3

Mass _____ g

Experimental mass density _____ $\dfrac{g}{cm^3}$

Accepted mass density _____ $\dfrac{g}{cm^3}$

Error _____ $\dfrac{g}{cm^3}$

% Error _____ %

Uniformly Accelerated Motion: Inclined Plane

THEORY

In the seventeenth century Galileo performed experiments which disproved the Aristotelian concept of motion of falling bodies. Specifically, Galileo challenged the premise established by Aristotle that a heavy object falls faster and reaches the ground earlier than a light object. Legend says that Galileo disproved this concept by dropping two spheres of different weights simultaneously from the top of the Leaning Tower of Pisa and observed that they reached the earth at the same time. While historians question the validity of this account, Galileo did perform a similar experiment for objects rolling down an inclined plane and extended the results to freely falling bodies.

Galileo was interested in more than disproving one specific result of the Aristotelian worldview; he was seeking a completely new description of motion. He proposed a bold new hypothesis of his own: that the motion of a falling body is determined by constant acceleration, and that this motion is not affected at all by the weight or mass of the body. This experiment is designed to examine Galileo's hypothesis, and to test its validity by experimenting in much the same way that he did.

In looking at the motion of a falling body, we can really measure only two things easily: the distance s traveled (which we can measure with a meterstick), and the time of fall t (which we can measure with a clock). Therefore, it is desirable to be able to look at acceleration in terms of time and distance. To do this step-by-step, we start with velocity. Velocity is defined as the change in displacement divided by the change in time, or:

$$v = \frac{\Delta x}{\Delta t} = \frac{x - x_o}{t - t_o} \tag{1}$$

Where x = final position, x_o = initial position, t = final time, and t_o = initial time.

In making a measurement, we can always arrange our meterstick so that the initial position is zero, and we can start our clock at the beginning of motion so that the initial time is also zero. Inserting these values into equation (1), we get the average velocity $\bar{v}$ of the motion as:

$$\bar{v} = \frac{x - 0}{t - 0} \quad \text{or,} \quad \bar{v} = \frac{x}{t} \tag{2}$$

Once we have defined velocity in terms of x and t, we can simply carry this one step further to define acceleration as the "change in velocity" for a given change in time."

Source: Puri
Modified by Zober and Zober

Purpose

To study uniformly accelerated motion.

Apparatus

Grooved inclined plane, meterstick, a glass marble and a steel marble, electronic timer, and graph paper.

$$a = \frac{\Delta v}{\Delta t} \quad \text{or,} \quad a = \frac{v - v_o}{t - t_o} \tag{3}$$

This is the quantity that Galileo claimed is constant in the motion of falling bodies. To make consequences of these as simple as possible, we arrange our experiment so that we start our clock at the beginning of motion, $t_o = 0$, and $t = t$, and we start the object falling from rest, $v_o = 0$. In this case equation (3) becomes:

$$a = \frac{v}{t} \quad \text{or,} \quad v = at \tag{4}$$

Although final velocity v cannot be measured directly, it can be calculated by using the equation for average velocity $\bar{v}$:

$$\bar{v} = \frac{v + v_o}{2} \tag{5}$$

By substituting this equation into our previous equation for average velocity we get:

$$\bar{v} = \frac{x}{t} = \frac{v + v_o}{2} \tag{6}$$

If $v_o = 0$, this yields,

$$\frac{x}{t} = \frac{v + 0}{2} \quad \text{or,} \quad v = \frac{2x}{t} \tag{7}$$

Finally, by combining equations (4) and (7), we find that

$$v = at = \frac{2x}{t} \quad \text{or,} \quad \frac{2x}{t} = at \quad \text{or,} \quad x = \frac{1}{2}at^2 \tag{8}$$

Now, if acceleration a is a constant, our final result says: the displacement of a falling body starting from rest is directly proportional to the time interval squared and is independent of the mass of the object. Thus, if Galileo is correct, a graph of x vs. t^2 should give a straight line with a slope of $\frac{1}{2}$ a.

Because of the experimental difficulty encountered in determining the time interval for a freely falling body, Galileo chose the inclined plane because the acceleration of gravity would be "diluted," thus allowing him to make a more accurate determination of time intervals using the waterclocks available to him. To make things easier for ourselves, we will use modern electronic timers instead. Galileo used a polished inclined plane with smooth balls. He released the balls from different positions along the inclined plane and timed their travel over given distances. After measuring the time intervals for various distances, Galileo discovered that the distance traveled by the balls and the square of the time of travel were indeed related by a direct proportionality. He repeated this experiment for different angles of inclination and found for each angle he obtained a new proportionality constant. Galileo observed that the proportionality constants increased as the angle of inclination increased. He asserted that, when the angle of inclination approached 90 degrees, the constant of proportionality would approach one-half the acceleration of a freely falling body as a consequence of equation (8).

The importance of Galileo's work with the inclined plane is found in its proof that all bodies, regardless of weight, fall with the same uniform acceleration. This proof aided him in refuting the Aristotelian physics of motion and represented a triumph of the scientific method that Galileo played such a great part in advancing.

LEARNING OBJECTIVES

After completing this experiment, you should be able to do the following:

1. Define and give an example of velocity.

2. Define and give an example of accelerated motion.

3. Explain how to find the velocity of an object in terms of distance traveled and time.

4. State the units of velocity and acceleration in the SI and English Systems.

5. State the relationship between the slope of your plotted graphs and the concepts of velocity and acceleration.

PROCEDURE

1. Practice starting the marbles and clock simultaneously a few times until you can time the marble's trip down the incline with some confidence. Start the marble rolling by setting it at some specified distance and holding it there with a pencil or ruler in front. You can start it by quickly removing the pencil. This will prevent you from accidentally giving the marble an extra push when you start it.

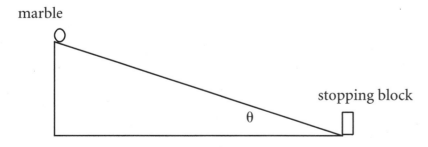

marble

θ

stopping block

Figure 3.1

2. Place the marble on the inclined track at the distance specified on your data sheet.

3. When the marble is released, start your electronic timer. When the marble strikes the stopping block, record the *elapsed time* in units of seconds.

4. Repeat your measurements for this distance two more times, recording the elapsed time in your data table.

5. Repeat the experiment for other distances in your data table.

6. Repeat the entire experiment for the lighter mass.

7. Plot graphs of distance vs. average time for each marble.

8. Make graphs of distance vs. average time squared for each marble.

9. Use your graphs to answer the questions given in the laboratory.

Questions

1. If you increase the inclination of the grooved track, will the marbles roll faster or slower? Why?

2. List the possible errors you cannot avoid in performing the experiment.

3. Why should you note the "elapsed time" three times?

4. Does the experimental result refute Aristotelian Physics of Motion?

5. If a ball falls 10 meters in 2 seconds, what is the acceleration?

6. What does the shape of the distance vs. $(time)^2$ graph indicate?

Uniformly Accelerated Motion: Inclined Plane

Name: _____   Date: _____

PART A.   HEAVY MARBLE

Distance	Elapsed time trial 1	Elapsed time trial 2	Elapsed time trial 3	Average time	Average time squared
cm	s	s	s	s	s^2
0					
20					
40					
60					
80					

PART B.   LIGHT MARBLE

Distance	Elapsed time trial 1	Elapsed time trial 2	Elapsed time trial 3	Average time	Average time squared
cm	s	s	s	s	s^2
0					
20					
40					
60					
80					

Composition and Resolution of Forces

THEORY

Scalar quantities are those that may be completely described by giving the magnitude of the quantity, such as length, mass, or density. To completely describe a vector quantity such as force a direction as well as a magnitude is needed. The question "What direction?" is as important as the question "How much?" A vector may be represented by a straight line segment drawn from some origin, with the length of the line proportional to the magnitude of the vector and the direction of the line represented by the tip of an arrow pointing in the direction of the vector (Fig 4.1).

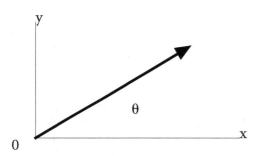

Figure 4.1

Vector may be combined by graphical or by analytical methods. The operation of adding vectors graphically consists of drawing one vector with appropriate length and direction, and from the head of this vector, another vector is drawn with appropriate length and direction, and so on, for as many vectors as are present. The straight line drawn from the origin to the head of the last vector represents the sum of the vectors and is called the *resultant* (Fig 4.2). This method is called the Polygon Method.

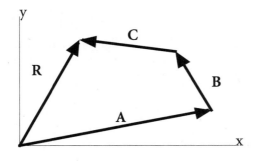

Figure 4.2

Source: Puri
Modified by Zober and Zober

Purpose

To use analytical, graphical, and experimental methods to determine the resultant and equilibrant of several sets of forces.

Apparatus

Force table, mass hangers and slotted masses, graph paper, ruler, and protractor.

Resultants represent a net or an unbalanced force. The systems that we study with the force table are systems in equilibrium. In a system in equilibrium the resultant force is zero. To nullify a resultant we must introduce a force called an *equilibrant*. The equilibrant is equal in magnitude to the resultant but is 180° away. The equilibrant is an antiparallel vector that nullifies or "cancels out" the resultant.

It is clear why a distinction is made between a scalar and a vector. Scalar quantities can be added algebraically to obtain a sum; vector quantities must be added by the rules of vector addition. The vector equation for Fig 4.2 is written as:

$$\mathbf{R} = \mathbf{A} + \mathbf{B} + \mathbf{C}$$

Every vector in 2 dimensional space has a set of two components, a horizontal or x-component and a vertical or a y-component. We may denote the components, which are vectors themselves, of a vector $\mathbf{A}$ as: $\mathbf{x}$ or $\mathbf{X}$ or $\mathbf{A}_x$ for the horizontal, and $\mathbf{y}$ or $\mathbf{Y}$ or $\mathbf{A}_y$ for the vertical. We show vectors that are in print as boldface characters, Fig. 4.3.

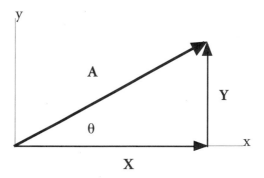

Figure 4.3

We can calculate the X and Y-components by using trig methods, and:

$$X = A \cos \theta \text{ and } Y = A \sin \theta \qquad (1)$$

When two or more force vectors act *concurrently* (at the same point) and *simultaneously* (at the same time), we may use a method called the *Vector Resolution* or simply the *Component Method* to find the resultant of the vectors. When you add all the x-components of all the vectors acting on the system and then add all the y-components of every vector, you get the sum of the components that are the components of the resultant.

$$\sum X = X_1 + X_2 + X_3 + \ldots + X_n \qquad (2)$$

and

$$\sum Y = Y_1 + Y_2 + Y_3 + \ldots + Y_n \qquad (3)$$

Here, equation (2) gives ΣX that is the x-component of the resultant and equation (3) gives ΣY, the y-component of the resultant. When using the component method to determine the resultant, always make a sketch of the components and the resultant as in Fig 4.4.

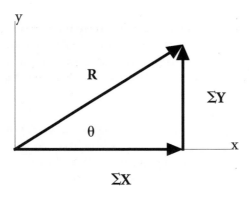

Figure 4.4

ΣX and ΣY are the components of the resultant, R. The resultant is found by using of the Pythagorean Theorem:

$$R^2 = \left(\sum X \right)^2 + \left(\sum Y \right)^2 \qquad (4)$$

and the magnitude of R is then:

$$R = \sqrt{\left(\sum X \right)^2 + \left(\sum Y \right)^2} \qquad (5)$$

The angle, θ, of the resultant is expressed as a tangent function, or:

$$\tan \theta = \frac{\sum Y}{\sum X} \qquad (6)$$

and the angle itself is:

$$\theta = \tan^{-1} \left| \frac{\sum Y}{\sum X} \right| \qquad (7)$$

Note that angle θ is the absolute value of the ratio. Taking the absolute value removes the signs of the components. From your sketch, as in Fig 4.4, you will know the quadrant of the resultant. All you need to do is to correct for the quadrant.

The equilibrant will equal the magnitude of the resultant but will be 180° away or simply in the opposite direction.

To calculate the equilibrant using the component method:

1. Use equations (1) to calculate the x and the y-component of each vector acting in the system.

2. Use equations (2) and (3) to find the sum of the components.

3. Sketch out a frame of reference and sketch in the x-component giving attention to the sign. At the tip of the x-component sketch in the y-component once again giving attention to the sign. Make a triangle by sketching a line from the origin to the tip of the y-component. This represents the resultant. Note the quadrant.

4. Use equation (5) and calculate the magnitude (size) of the resultant.

5. Use equation (7) to find the angle of R. θ_d is the direction from the reference axis.
If θ is in quadrant I, $\theta_d = \theta$.
If θ is in quadrant II, $\theta_d = 180° - \theta$.
If θ is in quadrant III, $\theta_d = \theta + 180°$.
If θ is in quadrant IV, $\theta_d = 360° - \theta$.

6. The magnitude of the equilibrant will equal the magnitude of the resultant. The angle of the equilibrant will be 180° away from the angle of the resultant.

LEARNING OBJECTIVES

After completing the experiment you should be able to do the following:

1. Define a vector.

2. Differentiate between a scalar and a vector and give examples of each.

3. Make a polygon diagram for the vector sum of several vectors.

4. Calculate the resultant of several vectors by using the component method.

5. Show what is necessary to place a body in equilibrium.

PROCEDURE

Note the following tables. Force units are dependent upon the system in use. In the SI, the unit is the newton, N. The English unit is the pound, lb. In this experiment we are going to invent a force unit called the gram force that we will abbreviate as g-force. We define this force unit as the force produced by a one-gram mass.

Problem number	F1	F2
No.	g-force	g-force
1	200@0°	150@75°
2	150@0°	250@300°
3	150@20°	150@120°
4	250@30°	150@120°
5	150@45°	250@150°
6	200@50°	250@135°

Table 1: Two Forces

Problem number	F1	F2	F3
No.	g-force	g-force	g-force
1	200@0°	200@60°	150@120°
2	250@0°	150@100°	200@210°
3	200@20°	200@90°	200@150°
4	200@30°	200@135°	250@220°
5	150@45°	200@90°	200@140°
6	250@60°	150@135°	150@300°

Table 2: Three Forces

Problem number	F1	F2	F3	F4
No.	g-force	g-force	g-force	g-force
1	150@0°	150@45°	200@100°	200@200°
2	200@10°	100@60°	100@145°	200@240°
3	220@20°	150@120°	150@270°	200@335°
4	170@30°	200@120°	100@210°	150@300°
5	200@30°	200@90°	220@150°	100@200°
6	160@45°	200@120°	180@180°	250@250°

Table 3: Four Forces

1. Choose two problems from Table 1, two problems from Table 2, and two problems from Table 3. If you are working in a lab group with others, each partner will choose two different problems from each table. Assuming that all of the forces in each problem are acting concurrently and simultaneously, use the:

(a) polygon method and find the resultant and then the equilibrant for each problem.
(b) component method and calculate the resultant and then the equilibrant for each problem.

2. Record the results of Procedure 1 in your data for Two Vector Solutions.

3. Setting the center pin on the force table in place, set the force table with three pulleys, two for the known forces from Table 1, and one for the equilibrant. Remember that the equilibrat will "balance" the know forces. We say that if the forces and equilibrant balance then the system is in a *State of Static Equilibrium*. Starting at 0°, move and position the pulleys in a counterclockwise manner. Set and "lock" each pulley at the given angle. Load each mass hanger with the proper mass. Be sure to include the mass of the mass hanger. In determining the experimental equilibrandt, load the third hanger and adjust the position until equilibrium is established. Remove the central pin. Is your system in equilibrium? Record this value.

4. Repeat the procedure for your second problem from Table 1.

5. Repeat procedure 3, this time fitting the force table with four pulleys: three for known forces from table 2, and one for the experimental equilibrant. Repeat again for the second problem from Table 2. Record in your data for Three Vector Solutions.

6. Repeat procedure 3, now fitting the force table with five pulleys: four for known forces from table 3, and one for the experimental equilibrant. Repeat again for the second problem from Table 3. Record in your data for Four Vector Solutions.

QUESTIONS

1. Given two concurrent and simultaneous forces acting on a body, F1 = 120 g-force @ 0° and F2 = 60 g-force @ 90°. Use the Pythagorean Theorem and the definition of the inverse tangent to calculate the resultant force acting on the body.

2. What force is required to place the body of question 1 into a state of static equilibrium?

3. What conditions are required to place a body into a state of static equilibrium? Explain in detail.

Composition and Resolution of Forces

Name: _____   Date: _____

TWO VECTOR SOLUTIONS

Problem	Graphic equilibrant	Analytical equilibrant	Experimental equilibrant
No.	Magnitude and direction	Magnitude and direction	Observation

THREE VECTOR SOLUTIONS

Problem	Graphic equilibrant	Analytical equilibrant	Experimental equilibrant
No.	Magnitude and direction	Magnitude and direction	Observation

THREE VECTOR SOLUTIONS

Problem	Graphic equilibrant	Analytical equilibrant	Experimental equilibrant
No.	Magnitude and direction	Magnitude and direction	Observation

The Acceleration Due to Gravity

THEORY

The acceleration in a time interval Δt is defined as

$$a = \frac{\Delta v}{\Delta t} = \frac{v - v_o}{t - t_o}$$

here v_o = initial velocity at time t_o, and v = final velocity at time t. If we start our timer at $t_o = 0$, then we may write $a = \frac{v - v_o}{t}$. Then we may write

$$v = v_o + at \qquad (1)$$

In free fall we consider motion along the y-axis. The point of release of a body will be the origin and its direction of motion will be along the −y-axis.

We have learned, in general, that $\bar{v} = \frac{s}{t} = \frac{v + v_o}{2}$, and for motion along the

y-axis this becomes $\bar{v} = \frac{y}{t} = \frac{v + v_o}{2}$. Now,

$$\frac{2y}{t} = v + v_o$$

And substituting v from equation (1) yields

$$\frac{2y}{t} = v_o + at + v_o = 2v_o + at$$

Dividing both sides by 2 and multiplying by t yields

$$y = v_o t + \frac{1}{2}at^2 \qquad (2)$$

Neglecting air resistance, bodies that fall in the earth's gravitational field fall with a uniform acceleration that we call the acceleration due to gravity. We write this as $a = -g$ since the motion is vertically downward for free fall. And finally we can write equation (2) as

$$y = v_o t - \frac{1}{2}gt^2 \qquad (3)$$

Source: Puri
Modified by Zober and Zober

Purpose

To experimentally determine the acceleration due to gravity.

Apparatus

Free fall timing device 60 Hz, timing tape, drop platform, C-clamps, double meterstick, masking tape, 200 g mass, and graph paper.

Equation (3) gives the vertical displacement of a body in free fall when starting from a fixed origin. Of course we choose a compact body and we release it from a point near the surface of the earth.

If a freely falling body is actually falling with constant acceleration (neglecting air resistance), equation (1) will give a straight line when v is plotted against t. Conversely, when such a graph is plotted, it will show that the acceleration is a constant; and the magnitude of the acceleration may be determined from the slope of the graph. To obtain data for such a graph, the body is released from rest and the position of the body is recorded for certain values of elapsed time. When plotted this data will give y vs. elapsed time for the body, and from this data the following may be calculated:

1. The average velocity of the body is obtained by dividing the distance fallen by the time.

2. The instantaneous velocity, v, is the slope of the tangent to a point on the distance vs. time graph.

3. The acceleration is the slope of the tangent to the velocity vs. time curve at the time instant considered.

4. The acceleration, whether it is constant or not, can be found by inspecting the velocity vs. time curve. If it is a constant, the velocity vs. time curve is a straight line and the average velocity is also the actual or instantaneous velocity at the mid-point of the time interval considered.

In this experiment, a 200 g mass with a timing tape attached to it is positioned at the top of a platform approximately 2 meters above the floor. The timing tape is threaded through an electronic timer that operates at 60 Hz. The mass is released and falls, pulling the tape through the timer. The timer fires every $\frac{1}{60}$ s leaving a record of the fall on the tape.

LEARNING OBJECTIVES

After completing this experiment you should be able to do the following:

1. Define displacement, velocity, and acceleration.

2. Give the SI units for displacement.

3. Show that the slope of a v vs. t graph yields acceleration.

4. Show that equation (3) is dimensionally correct.

PROCEDURE

Part of this experiment is to design your own data sheets. Study the procedures to decide how you will do these data sheets.

1. Mount a platform to the lab table that gives a two-meter drop to the floor. Position the timer at the edge of the platform but do not plug it in.

2. Using the double meterstick, measure the distance from the top of the platform to the floor. Add 40 cm to this distance and measure out a piece of timer tape to that length.

3. Place a notebook at the impact point beneath the timer to buffer the falling mass.

4. Thread the timer tape through the timer. Use a piece of masking tape to attach the 200-g mass to the end of the tape protruding from the timer. Take the slack from the tape and hold it in place with a finger at the far end of the platform.

5. Plug in the timing device. Energize it and then release the tape. As the mass falls to the floor pulling the tape behind it, the timer, every 1/60 of a second, sends an electrical pulse through the tape leaving a small burn point. The burn marks on the tape will appear as a series of dots on the tape.

6. Carefully spread the timer tape on the laboratory table and tape down its ends. As the tape begins it downward motion the first few dots form a small cluster. Pick the first distinguishable dot divorced from the rest of the cluster. Circle it and label as dot 1.

7. Circle every other dot labeling them in sequence. Since we are using every other dot the timing interval becomes

$$\frac{1}{60}s + \frac{1}{60}s = \frac{1}{30}s$$

8. Place the edge of the double meterstick along the line of dots. Once positioned, do not move the double meterstick until all of the dots have been measured. As precisely as possible, read the meterstick marking adjacent to each circled dot. Record these measurements in your data in the column for total distance. We will only measure the first 1.5 meters from the first dot.

9. The change in distance, Δx, between any two consecutive circled dots is found by taking differences,

$$\Delta x = x_2 - x_1$$

$$\Delta x = x_3 - x_2$$

$$\Delta x = x_4 - x_3$$

etc.

Carry out these subtractions and record your differences in the column marked Δx, distance between intervals.

10. The distance between any two-circled dots also represents a definite time interval, 1/30 s. The average speed through each interval is

$$\bar{v} = \frac{\Delta x}{\Delta t} = \frac{\Delta x}{\frac{1}{30}s} = 30(\Delta x)$$

11. Use this equation and calculate $\bar{v}$ for each time interval. In your data, record $\bar{v}$ between time intervals.

12. The change in speed, Δv, across an interval is found by subtracting, or

$$\Delta v = v_2 - v_1$$

$$\Delta v = v_3 - v_2$$

$$\Delta v = v_4 - v_3$$

etc.

calculate Δv for each interval and record these values in your data.

13. We define acceleration as the change in speed divided by the time interval, or

$$a = \frac{\Delta v}{\Delta t} = \frac{\Delta v}{1/30s} = 30(\Delta v)$$

Calculate the average acceleration for each time interval and record.

14. Average your values of acceleration, a. This average value is your experimental acceleration due to gravity. Use 980 $\frac{m}{s^2}$ as the accepted value and compare this to your experimental value. What is the error? What is the percent error?

15. Plot $\bar{v}$ vs. t. Find the slope of the curve. Compare the slope to your experimental acceleration due to gravity and the accepted value. What is the error? What is the percent error?

16. Plot a second graph of the total distance x vs. t. What does this curve show?

QUESTIONS

1. If a 100 g mass is used in place of the 200 g mass in the experiment, would you find a different value for the acceleration due to gravity? Explain.

2. A compact body is thrown vertically downward with a speed of 10 m/s from the roof of a building that is 20 meters high. Neglecting air resistance, what is the acceleration of the body? How long does it take the body to reach the ground? What is the velocity of the body upon impact?

3. Repeat Question 2 this time throwing the body vertically upward at 10 m/s.

Friction

THEORY

Friction is a contact force acting between two bodies as they move across each other or impend to move across each other. Friction acts opposite to the direction of motion or impending motion and is parallel to the surfaces in contact. Experiments have shown, for a solid on a solid, what factors determine the magnitude of the frictional force.

Friction is directly proportional to the normal force pressing the surfaces together. The normal force is applied by the surface on the body and is in reaction to the other vertical forces that are applied to the body. A free body diagram and a Newton's first law equation, $\Sigma F_y = 0$, is written to solve for the normal force.

Friction depends on the nature of the materials in contact. On the microscopic level the surfaces are rough. As the bodies move across each other the "hills and valleys" of their surfaces snag and impede the motion. Sanding the surfaces can reduce this snagging. However, as the surfaces become smoother, attractive forces of cohesion and adhesion play a much larger role. (Cohesive forces are forces between like molecules; adhesive forces are between unlike molecules. Water will bead on a waxed car because cohesion is greater than adhesion, but will lie flat on bare metal since adhesion is greater than cohesion.) These two forces account for about 70% of the contact force. Also present are spot welds between the surfaces and these too need to be overcome.

The coefficient of friction, μ, is the ratio of the frictional force to the normal

$$\mu = \frac{f}{N}$$

and it is dimensionless.

Starting friction is generally greater than kinetic friction. We will refer to kinetic friction as sliding friction. (Rolling friction exists; it is less than sliding friction, but we will not deal with it in this experiment.) The relationship between the frictional force, the normal, and the surface is an experimental relationship not a fundamental equation. Kinetic friction is given by

$$f_k = \mu_k N$$

and can have only one value.

Purpose

To determine the coefficients of friction μ_s and μ_k acting between two bodies.

Apparatus

Friction block, friction board, mass hanger, slotted masses, pulley and pulley clamp, string, balance, support rod with clamp, and a meterstick.

Static friction is defined as

$$f_s \leq \mu_s N$$

For solid on solid, friction is independent of surface area if all sides of the body are of uniform smoothness. The pressure

$$P = \frac{F}{A}$$

is large when the body is on end, while the area is small. On a side, the area is larger and the pressure is smaller. These tend to produce the same effect. Friction, for solid on solid, is also independent of speed.

LEARNING OBJECTIVES

After completing the experiment you should be able to do the following:

1. Define what the normal force means.

2. Be able to distinguish between static friction and kinetic friction.

3. Define the coefficient of friction.

4. Set up and solve free body diagrams for (a) the normal and (b) frictional force.

5. Explain the limiting angle of repose by making a diagram and by writing an equation.

PROCEDURE

PART A. THE COEFFICIENT OF STATIC FRICTION

1. Mass the block; record its mass in kilograms. Then convert the mass to weight by using w = mg.

2. With the surface of the friction board horizontal place the friction block on the far end of the board. Attach a string to the block and pass this string over the pulley to the mass hanger. Make sure that the string is horizontal as it passes over the pulley.

3. Add enough mass, the minimum mass, to the hanger so that when the board is tapped next to the block, the block *just* begins to slide. Record the total mass on the string and enter this into your data table. Use w = mg to convert this to newtons. Record this as $(f_s)_{max}$, the force of static friction.

4. Repeat procedure 2 by adding masses of 250 g, 500 g, 750 g, and 1000 g to the friction block. In each case determine the maximum force of static friction.

5. Calculate the coefficient of static friction for the five trials and record the average value as your experimental value.

6. Plot a graph of f_s vs. N and determine the slope of the line.

PART B.   THE COEFFICIENT OF KINETIC FRICTION

7. Use the same friction block and the same arrangement as you did in Part A. Adjust the load on the hanger so that *after the block is started,* it will continue to move at constant speed across the board. Record the total mass on the string and enter this into your data table. Use w = mg to convert this to newtons. Record this as the force of kinetic friction f_k. Also record the normal force acting on the block.

8. Repeat procedure 4 from Part A. Record the frictional force in each trial and the normal force acting on the block.

9. Calculate the coefficient of kinetic friction for each trial and record the average value as your experimental value.

10. Plot a graph of f_k vs. N and determine the slope of the line.

PART C.   EXPERIMENTAL DETERMINATION OF THE SLIP ANGLE OF THE INCLINE PLANE

11. Remove the cord and the mass hanger from the friction block. Locate the hole through the plane of the friction board. Align the hole with the support clamp and slide the friction board on to the clamp. Place the empty friction block near the top of the incline plane. By trial and error adjust the plane to the minimum angle so that when the plane is tapped adjacent to the block, the block just slides down the plane. This is *the slip angle.*

12. Carefully, using the meterstick, measure the length of the plane and the vertical distance from the end of the plane to the tabletop. Make a diagram and record your data. Find the angle and record.

13. Repeat four more times and determine the average experimental slip angle.

14. Make a free body diagram of the body on the tilted inclined plane. Identify all the forces acting on the block. Write the $\Sigma F = 0$ equation and solve for the coefficient of friction.

15. Compare this value with the average experimental coefficient of friction in Part A.

QUESTIONS

1. Can the normal force ever be greater than the weight? If so, when?

2. Can the normal force ever be less than the weight? If so, when?

3. What is the effective weight of the block in Part C of the experiment? What is the value for the frictional force in Part C of the experiment?

4. Can the coefficient of static friction ever be less than the coefficient of kinetic friction?

5. Can the coefficient of friction ever be greater than 1?

Friction

Name: _____   Date: _____

Friction block mass_____   Friction block weight_____

PART A:

Trial	Mass on hanger	Weight on hanger	Normal force	Coefficient μ_s
No.	g	N	N	—
1				
2				
3				
4				
5				

Part B.

Trial	Mass on hanger	Weight on hanger	Normal force	Coefficient μ_k
No.	g	N	N	—
1				
2				
3				
4				
5				

Part C.

Trial	Length of plane	Height of plane	Plane angle
No.	cm	cm	degrees
1			
2			
3			
4			
5			

Newton's Second Law of Motion

THEORY

Newton's Second Law demonstrates that the acceleration of a body that is free to move is directly proportional to the net force acting upon it and is in the same direction as the force.

$$\sum F \propto a$$

Furthermore, Newton recognized that the inertia of the body (its mass) plays a role in its acceleration, and the acceleration is inversely proportional to the mass, or

$$a \propto \frac{1}{m}$$

Combining the relationships yields

$$\sum F \propto ma$$

We define the SI unit of force, the newton, N, as the net force that produces an acceleration of $1 \frac{m}{s^2}$ when applied to a body of 1 kilogram mass. Newton's Second Law becomes

$$\sum F = ma \qquad (1)$$

The weight of a body is determined by

$$w = mg \qquad (2)$$

At first inspection this looks like a rewrite of Newton's Second Law applied to a body with a gravitational acceleration. However, this is not the case. The mass in equation (1) is an inertial mass; the mass in equation (2) is a gravitational mass. They are different quantities because they have different defining equations

$$m_{inertial} = \frac{\sum F}{a} \quad \text{and} \quad m_{gravitational} = \frac{w}{g}$$

They are independent and proportional. Since the proportionality constant between them is one, they are equivalent. Therefore we can replace an inertial mass in an equation by a gravitational mass. Equation (1) may be written as

Purpose

To determine experimentally the relationship between force, acceleration and mass.

Apparatus

Cart, recording timer, timer tape, pulley, pulley clamp, mass hanger, and slotted masses.

Source: Zober and Zober

$$\sum F = \frac{w}{g}a$$

and we can substitute the weight on the pulley in this experiment for force.

$$\sum F = (mg - f) = Ma$$

where M is the mass of the cart.

LEARNING OBJECTIVES

After completing this experiment, you should be able to do the following:

1. Be able to draw a free body diagram showing the forces acting on a body.

2. Be able to write and solve the equation of motion of a body from a free body diagram.

3. State the units for force in the SI system.

4. Know the unit for mass in the SI system is kg and force is N, and be able to correctly convert between the two of them.

5. Know that weight will vary from location to location since the value for gravity will change, but the mass of the body is constant.

PROCEDURE

Part of this experiment is to design your own data sheets. Study the procedures to decide how you will do these data sheets.

1. Mass the cart, M, and record this value in your data table.

2. Determine the time interval of your timer.

3. Place the cart on the laboratory table. Attach a timer tape and thread it through the timer, but do not turn on the timer. Attach a string to the other end of the cart and pass this string over the pulley making sure that the string is parallel to the table. Attach a mass hanger to the free end.

4. Adjust the mass on the pulley so that the system will move at constant speed when the cart is given a slight push. Set up and solve a Newton's first law equation $\sum F = 0$ and solve for the effective frictional force (between the tape and timer and the cart and the laboratory table).

$$\sum F = 0$$

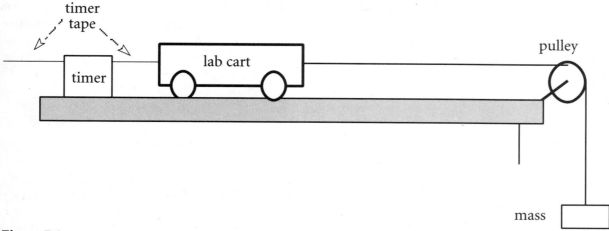

Figure 7.1

and,

$$F_{pulley} - f = 0$$

Record the total mass on the hanger being careful to add the mass of the hanger. Convert the mass to a weight and record.

5. Increase the mass added to the pulley. The force acting on the system is now greater than the frictional force and the cart will accelerate. Turn on the timer, and release the cart.

6. Mark the timer tape as "Run # 1". Record the force on the pulley for Run # 1 on the tape and in your data table.

7. Repeat the procedure for three additional forces, marking the tapes, Run #2, #3, and # 4.

8. Evaluate the timer tapes, determining velocity by the alternative method indicated below.

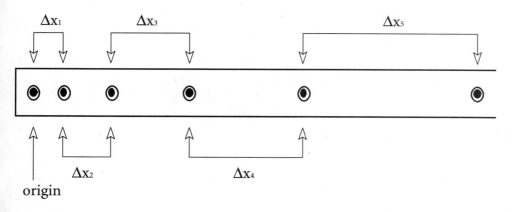

Figure 7.2

9. We will add two intervals and divide by 2t. This gives us average velocity. Since the cart is uniformly accelerated this average velocity will approximate the velocity at the midpoint of the two intervals

$$\frac{\Delta x_1 + \Delta x_2}{2t} \cong v_1$$

$$\frac{\Delta x_2 + \Delta x_3}{2t} \cong v_2$$

$$\frac{\Delta x_3 + \Delta x_4}{2t} \cong v_3$$

and so on. Calculate the velocity for the first 15 dots after your origin and record in the data table. Repeat this for the other three time tapes.

10. Plot a graph of v vs. t. Plot all 4 runs on the same graph paper. Take the slope of each line and determine the experimental value for the acceleration of each run. Compare the experimental values to the ones calculated from

$$\sum F = ma$$

and,

$$F_{pulley} - f = ma$$

QUESTIONS

1. Why was it necessary to determine the friction of the system before you generated any timer tapes?

2. Was it necessary for you to start your measurements from the first dot on the timer tape?

3. How would you determine the relationship between mass and acceleration if you were given a constant force?

4. How would you determine the value of an unknown force applied to the cart?

5. A 25 N force acts on a 3.5 kg mass accelerating it in a location where the friction between the cart and the surface is 4.8N. What is the velocity of the cart after it has traveled 12.6m?

The Atwood Machine

THEORY

When two unequal masses are connected with a light, strong cord that passes over a pulley of negligible mass, the arrangement is called Atwood's machine. George Atwood, in 1784, described the device shown in Figure 8.1 as one for diluting and measuring the acceleration due to gravity.

Purpose

To study Newton's Second Law of Motion by the use of the Atwood's Machine.

Apparatus

Simple Atwood's machine, stop watch, two mass hangers, light, strong fishing line, slotted masses, double meterstick.

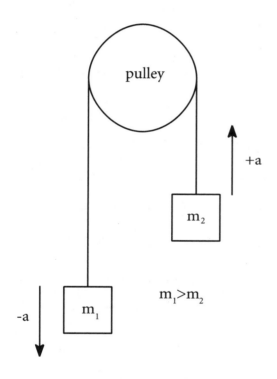

pulley

+a

m_2

$m_1 > m_2$

-a

m_1

Figure 8.1

If $m_1 > m_2$ and the system is released from rest, the entire system will have the same acceleration. Pulleys change the direction of tension vectors, and the magnitude of the tension everywhere in the cord has the same value. A free body diagram of the two masses in the system, Figure 8.2, will allow us to analyze the motion of the system.

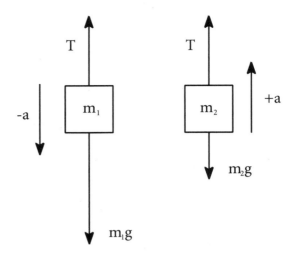

Figure 8.2

Writing Newton's second law for mass m_1: $\Sigma F = m_1 a$, and,

$$T - m_1 g = m_1(-a)$$

The tension in the cord is then

$$T = m_1 g - m_1 a$$

Writing Newton's second law for mass m_2: $\Sigma F = m_2 a$, and,

$$T - m_2 g = m_2 a$$

The tension is

$$T = m_2 g + m_2 a$$

Since the tension in the cord equals itself,

$$m_1 g - m_1 a = m_2 g + m_2 a$$

separating variables,

$$m_1 a + m_2 a = m_1 g - m_2 g$$

factoring,

$$a(m_1 + m_2) = g(m_1 - m_2)$$

And solving for a we have

$$a = \left(\frac{m_1 - m_2}{m_1 + m_2}\right)g \tag{1}$$

Equation (1) will allow us to calculate the acceleration of the Atwood machine.

From our study of free fall we have,

$$y = v_0 t + \frac{1}{2}at^2 \qquad\qquad (2)$$

And when starting from rest where $v_0 = 0$,

$$y = \frac{1}{2}at^2$$

LEARNING OBJECTIVES

After completing this experiment you should be able to do the following:

1. Define and give an example of a multi-mass system accelerated by a net force.

2. Make a free body diagram for the forces acting on each body in the system.

3. Recognize that mass is measured in kilograms and weight is measured in Newtons in the SI system.

4. Solve with correct conversions in both the SI and the CGS system those equations containing the mass or weight of a body moving in a gravitational field.

PROCEDURE

1. Use a *total* mass of 1500 g to 2000 g on the mass hangers. This total mass is to remain constant throughout the experiment.

2. Determine the force of friction on the pulley by transferring mass from one side to the other side until the system moves at constant speed when given a slight push. Calculate the frictional force on the pulley by subtracting the two masses. Record this value.

3. Before you run your trials, arrange the masses on the ascending side so that you have five two-g masses that can be transferred to the descending side.

4. Transfer the first 2.0 g mass from the ascending side to the descending side. You now have a net force of 3.92×10^{-2} N acting on the system. Begin the experiment with the ascending mass on the floor. Release the descending mass, stopping the timer when it reaches the floor. Record the time and the distance between the two masses. Repeat for two more trials. Determine and record the average of these times. Calculate the acceleration of the system using equation (3).

5. Transfer another 2.0 g mass from the ascending side to the descending side. Repeat the procedure in the step above, again making three separate determinations of the time.

6. Continue transferring mass from the ascending side to the descending side until you have transferred a total of 10.0 g.

7. Compute the acceleration of the system using $\sum F_y = ma_y$ for each trial. Compare the two values.

8. Using the acceleration of procedure 4, plot a graph of acceleration vs. $\dfrac{(m_1 - m_2)}{m_1 + m_2}$
Compute the experimental value for the acceleration due to gravity and compare to the accepted value.

QUESTIONS

1. What advantage, if any, is there in transferring mass from one side to another?

2. Account for the difference between your experimental and calculated values for the acceleration, a, of the system.

3. Calculate the tension in the string supporting the masses. Is it the same on both sides of the string? Should it be? Why or why not?

4. Why should the pulley be as light as possible? You may have to read ahead in your textbook to answer this question.

The Atwood Machine

Name: _____   Date: _____

Mass on the system:

m_1 _____

m_2 _____

Friction on the pulley _____

Descent distance _____

Trial	Mass transfered	Mass difference $m_1 - m_2$	Net force	Time 1	Time 2	Time 3	Average time	Experimental acceleration
No.	m	Δm	F	t_1	t_2	t_3	t_{ave}	a_{exp}
—	g	g	N	s	s	s	s	m s^{-2}
1								
2								
3								
4								
5								

Elastic Collisions

THEORY

When two bodies collide, a small amount of energy is expended due to the deformation of the bodies. If the collision is elastic, all the energy expended in changing the shape of the objects is recovered. In the case of a perfectly elastic collision, the kinetic energy of the total system containing all the objects remains constant. In this experiment the conservation of momentum and the conservation of kinetic energy will be examined for an elastic collision.

In any collision, momentum is always conserved. Kinetic energy may or may not be conserved, depending on the nature of the objects involved. Perfectly elastic collisions can take place between atoms and subatomic particles but on a macroscopic scale, for objects of ordinary size, perfectly elastic collisions do not occur. However, if the objects involved in the collisions are sufficiently rigid, then the amount of kinetic energy lost is very small and the collision, for all practical purposes can be considered elastic.

When a particle of mass m moving with a velocity $\vec{v_1}$ collides with a second particle of the same mass that is at rest, the conservation of momentum gives

$$m\vec{v_1} + m(0) = m\vec{V_1} + m\vec{V_2}$$

where $\vec{V_1}$ and $\vec{V_2}$ are the velocities of the two particles after the collision. If the collision is elastic, then the conservation of kinetic energy can be invoked and

$$\frac{1}{2} m|\vec{v_1}|^2 + \frac{1}{2} m(0)^2 = \frac{1}{2} m|\vec{V_1}|^2 + \frac{1}{2} m|\vec{V_2}|^2$$

For a head-on collision, all the momentum and all the kinetic energy of the first particle is transferred to the second and the first particle has a zero velocity after the collision. In this case the two conservation equations result in

$$m\vec{v_1} + 0 = 0 + m\vec{V_2}$$

$$\vec{v_1} = \vec{V_2} \tag{1}$$

$$\frac{1}{2} m|\vec{v_1}|^2 + 0 = \frac{1}{2} m|\vec{V_2}|^2$$

$$|\vec{v_1}|^2 = |\vec{V_2}|^2 \tag{2}$$

Source: Ramirez
Modified by Zober and Zober

Purpose

(a) To evaluate elastic collisions between bodies of equal masses.

Apparatus

Grooved track, 2 steel balls, large sheet of paper (2 ft by 2 ft), carbon paper, meterstick, and a protractor.

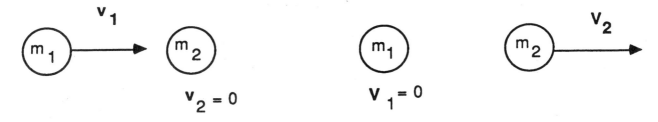

head-on collision

Figure 9.1

So for a head-on collision with equal masses, the velocity of particle 2 after the collision is equal in magnitude and is in the same direction as the velocity of particle 1 before the collision.

If the collision is a glancing collision, only part of the energy and momentum of particle 1 is transferred to particle 2. In this case, conservation of energy and momentum result in

$$m\vec{v_1} + 0 = m\vec{V_1} + m\vec{V_2}$$

$$\vec{v_1} = \vec{V_1} + \vec{V_2} \tag{3}$$

$$\frac{1}{2}m|\vec{v_1}|^2 + 0 = \frac{1}{2}m|\vec{V_1}|^2 + \frac{1}{2}m|\vec{V_2}|^2$$

$$|\vec{v_1}|^2 = |\vec{V_1}|^2 + |\vec{V_2}|^2 \tag{4}$$

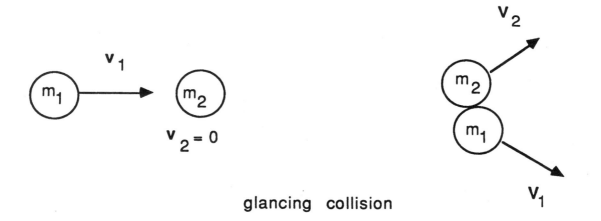

glancing collision

Figure 9.2

Suppose the collision between the two particles occurs at some height above the ground and that after the collision the particles are allowed to fall. If the initial velocity of particle 1 is horizontal and particle 2 is initially at rest, then immediately after the collision the velocities of the two particles will still be in the horizontal direction. The horizontal position of the particles as they follow a trajectory to the ground will be given by

$$\vec{x}(t) = \vec{x}(0) + \vec{v_x}(0)\, t$$

$$\vec{x_1}(t) = \vec{V_1}\, t$$

$$\vec{x_2}(t) = \vec{V_2}\, t$$

$$\vec{V_1} = \frac{\vec{x_1}(t)}{t}$$

$$\vec{V_2} = \frac{\vec{x_2}(t)}{t} \tag{5}$$

The velocities of the two particles therefore are proportional to the horizontal distance they travel after the impact. Since the particles are at the same height when they collide, the fall time, t, is the same for both and a measurement of $\vec{x}(t)$ provides all the information necessary to examine the conservation of momentum and kinetic energy.

LEARNING OBJECTIVES

After completing the experiment, you should be able to do the following:

1. Define an elastic collision.

2. Recognize that momentum is a vector quantity while kinetic energy is a scalar.

3. Recognize that velocity has magnitude and direction.

4. Use projectile motion to solve for the range in the incident steel ball in the collision.

5. Recognize that for both head-on collisions and glancing collisions, the range of the bodies can be used to solve for momentum.

6. Use energy and momentum equations in analyzing both head-on and glancing collisions.

PROCEDURE

The elastic collision apparatus consists of a grooved track mounted on a wooden base. One of the steel balls (called the projectile since it will be projected along the track) is held against a small metal stop at the upper end of the track until it is ready to be released. At the lower end of the track is a movable target support that will hold the second steel ball (the target ball). The horizontal and vertical positions of the screw can be adjusted to allow for glancing, head-on and no collisions.

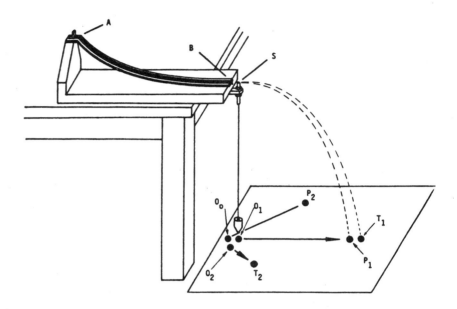

Figure 9.3

Tape a large (2′ × 2′) piece of paper to the floor near the table so that it is centered under the apparatus and extends several inches back under the edge of the table. Be sure that the paper does not move during the experiment.

A. DETERMINING THE INITIAL VELOCITY OF THE PROJECTILE (NO COLLISION)

1. Take one of the steel balls and hold it at the top of the grooved track at point A. This is the projectile. Loosen the lock nuts on the target support and move it to the side so that the projectile will not strike the support as it leaves the track and falls to the floor. Release the projectile and note where it strikes the paper that was placed on the floor. Place a piece of carbon paper face down at the approximate point where the projectile landed. Release the projectile from the top of the track six times. Be sure it strikes the carbon paper and leaves a mark on the paper underneath each time.

2. Remove the carbon paper and surround the six dots with a very lightly drawn circle and draw a line through each dot. The circle does not need to be exact, it will only be used to temporarily distinguish these marks from those made later in the experiment. Label this set of points P_1.

B. HEAD-ON COLLISION

1. Move the target support so that it is directly in the path of the projectile. The support must be centered exactly along the axis of the track and not moved to one side or the other. Place one steel ball, the target ball, on the support and place the projectile as close as possible to the end of the track. In order to obtain a head-on collision, the two balls must be at the same height when they collide. Adjust the target support until the two balls are at the same height. In addition, the projectile must strike the target just as the projectile leaves the track. This means that the target support should be adjusted so that the two balls are touching when the projectile is just resting on the edge of the track. Check once again that the two balls are at the same height and are aligned along the axis of the track. Clamp the target support in place by tightening the nut screws under the target support.

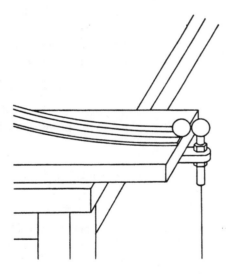

Figure 9.4

2. Place the target on the support. Release the projectile from point A and note where the target lands after the collision. It should fall at a point at or just beyond P_1. If it lands too short or too much to the side, check the alignment of the target support once more to be certain that the collision is head-on.

3. Place the carbon paper face down. Place the target on the support and release the projectile from point A. Do this six times. Remove the carbon paper and lightly circle the six new points for the head-on collision. Call this T_1.

4. In order to indicate the position of the target before the collision, lower the plumb bob on the target support until its point just touches the paper. Place the carbon paper under the point and carefully put enough pressure on the plumb bob to put an impression on the paper. Darken this point with a pen or pencil if necessary and label it O_1.

C. GLANCING COLLISION

1. For the glancing collision, the target support should be moved to one side so that the projectile, when released, will just barely strike the target. Place the target on the support and release the projectile from point A. Note where the two balls land (do not use the carbon paper yet). Adjust the target support until the target has about one-half the horizontal range as the projectile (as seen on the paper). The target holder should still be adjusted so that the two balls are at the same height. Again the two balls should be touching when the projectile is at the edge of the track and is just about to leave it. Tighten the lock nuts on the target support once it has been properly aligned.

2. Place two sheets of carbon paper on the large sheet of paper where the target and the projectile land. Place the target on the support and release the projectile from point A. Record six glancing collisions.

3. Lightly circle each set of points for the glancing collision. Label the points made by the target ball as T_2 and the points made by the projectile as P_2.

4. Use the plumb bob as before to mark the position of the center of the target during the glancing collision. Label the point made by the plumb bob as O_2.

5. Have your instructor check the large sheet of paper before it is removed from the floor.

6. Replace the two steel balls in their holders and remove the large sheet of paper from the floor.

D. VECTOR ANALYSIS

1. Using the compass provided, draw a circle around the points labeled P_1, T_1, P_2, T_2. The circles should be as small as possible yet still enclose all of the points. Clearly indicate the center of each circle. The radius of each circle will be a measure of the uncertainty.

2. Draw a straight line from point P_1 to point O_1 and extend it back 1.27 *cm* (the diameter of one steel ball) past O_1. Label this point O_0. This is the position of the center of the projectile when it is on the very edge of the track and just about to strike the target.

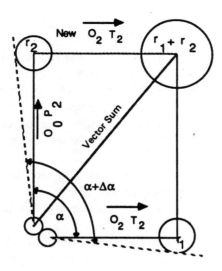

Figure 9.5

3. Using the meter stick, measure and record the length of $\overrightarrow{O_0P_1}$. Measure and record the length of $\overrightarrow{O_1T_1}$. Measure and record the uncertainties of each of these lines.

4. Determine the difference (and its uncertainty) in the lengths of the lines $\overrightarrow{O_0P_1}$ and $\overrightarrow{O_1T_1}$. Record the angle between $\overrightarrow{O_0P_1}$ and $\overrightarrow{O_1T_1}$ as the difference in the direction for the two vectors.

5. Draw the lines $\overrightarrow{O_0P_2}$ and $\overrightarrow{O_2T_2}$. Measure and record the lengths and the uncertainties in the lengths of these two lines.

6. Measure and record the angle α $(P_2O_0T_2)$ between the lines $\overrightarrow{O_0P_2}$ and $\overrightarrow{O_2T_2}$. Using the error circles, determine and record the angle $\alpha + \Delta\alpha$.

7. Add the two vectors produced by the glancing collision by drawing the vector $\overrightarrow{O_2T_2}$ at the tip of $\overrightarrow{O_0P_2}$. Use the angle a and the length measured in procedure (6).

8. Draw a line connecting O_0 to the tip of the vector (the new $\overrightarrow{O_2T_2}$ just drawn). This is the vector sum of $\overrightarrow{O_0P_2}$ and $\overrightarrow{O_2T_2}$.

9. Measure and record the length of the vector sum. Determine and record the error associated with the vector sum. Determine the difference in the lengths (and its uncertainty) for the vector sum and $\overrightarrow{O_0P_2}$. Record the difference in direction of the vector sum and $\overrightarrow{O_0P_2}$.

Questions

According to equation (5), the velocities of the target and the projectile in a collision are proportional to the horizontal range of each. This range is represented by the vectors drawn on the large sheet of paper in the vector analysis section of the procedure. So when the velocities are used to determine whether the momentum and the kinetic energy are conserved, a comparison of the range vectors will provide all the necessary information.

For example if two vectors on the paper have the same length, then the magnitudes of the velocities were equal. Likewise, if two distance vectors have the same orientation, then the two velocities also had identical directions.

In answering the following questions, be sure to include equations and to use the numerical results from the vector analysis to support your answers. Include units and uncertainties for all quantities. If you show no numerical justifications for your conclusions, your answers will not be accepted.

1. Was momentum conserved (to within experimental uncertainty) in the head-on collision? See equation (1).

2. Was kinetic energy conserved (to within experimental uncertainty) in the head-on collision? See equation (2).

3. Was momentum conserved (to within experimental uncertainty) in the glancing collision? See equation (3).

4. Was kinetic energy conserved (to within experimental uncertainty) in the glancing collision? See equation (4).

Elastic Collisions

Name: _____   Lab Section #: _____

Date: _____   Lab Partners: _____

D.   VECTOR ANALYSIS

(3) $\overrightarrow{O_0P_1}$ = _____ ± _____ (no collision)

(4) $\overrightarrow{O_1T_1}$ = _____ ± _____ (head-on collision)

   Difference in length _____ ± _____

   Difference in direction _____

(5) $\overrightarrow{O_0P_2}$ = _____ ± _____

   $\overrightarrow{O_2T_2}$ = _____ ± _____

(6) α = _____

   $\alpha + \Delta\alpha$ = _____

(9) Vector Sum

   $\overrightarrow{O_0P_2} + \overrightarrow{O_2T_2}$ = _____ ± _____ (glancing collision)

   $\overrightarrow{O_0P_1}$ = _____ ± _____ (no collision)

   Difference in length _____ ± _____

   Difference in direction _____

Inelastic Collisions

THEORY

Collisions may be classified as either elastic or inelastic in nature. For all systems containing two or more bodies, the total linear momentum of the system during a collision will remain constant as long as no external forces are applied to the system. In an inelastic collision, the total energy and the momentum of the system are conserved. If, in addition to the total energy and the momentum, the kinetic energy of the system is also conserved, then the collision is elastic. In this experiment, the ballistic pendulum will be used to study the conservation of momentum for an inelastic collision.

Whenever an external force acts on an object, its momentum is changed, the time rate of change being proportional to the average net applied force:

$$\frac{\Delta \vec{p}}{\Delta t} = (\vec{Fext})_{av}$$

So according to Newton's laws of motion, the linear momentum of a system of objects will remain constant when the net external force acting on the system remains zero. In all impacts, objects exert equal and opposite forces on each other when they come into contact. Thus when the momentum of one object is changed, the momentum of the other object undergoes a change of the same magnitude but of the opposite direction. Thus, the total momentum before the collision will equal to the total momentum after the collision. This is a statement of the conservation of linear momentum.

A completely inelastic impact can be demonstrated when two objects collide and adhere, moving off with a common velocity after the impact. Consider the case in which one object of mass m_1 moving with a velocity $\vec{v_1}$ strikes a second object of mass m_2 which is initially at rest.

Purpose

To demonstrate the conservation of momentum for an inelastic collision.

Apparatus

Ballistic pendulum, platform box, meter stick, target box, 2-meter stick, plumb bob, vertical distance marker, and carbon paper.

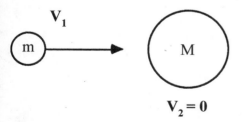

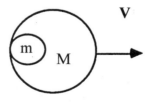

before the collision   after the collision

Figure 10.1

If the two objects share a common velocity $\vec{V}$, after the impact, then the conservation of momentum gives

$$\vec{P}_{\text{before}} = \vec{P}_{\text{after}}$$

$$m_1\vec{v_1} + m_2\,(0) = (m_1 + m_2)\,\vec{V} \tag{1}$$

$$mV_1 + M(0) = (m + M)V$$

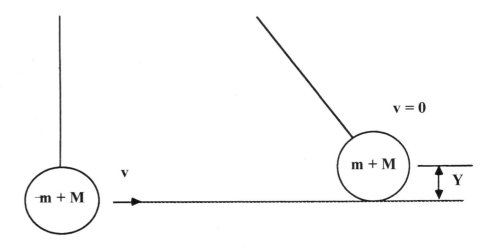

Figure 10.2

In order to determine the momentum, the velocities (or speeds since the velocities are in the same direction) of the two objects must be determined. One method used to determine the speeds utilizes the conservation of mechanical energy. In this case m embeds itself in M and the combined mass is allowed to rise through a vertical height Y. The conservation of mechanical energy states that the kinetic energy of the two masses immediately after the impact is totally converted into potential energy as the system rises to its highest point. If the initial velocity of the particles at their lowest point immediately after the impact is V and the particle system swings through a height Y, then

$$\frac{1}{2}(m + M)\,V^2 = (m + M)\,gY$$

$$V^2 = 2gY$$

$$V = \sqrt{2gY} \tag{2}$$

Substituting this into equation (1) generates a value for the initial velocity of particle 1 in terms of the height to which the combined masses rise.

$$mv = (m + M) \sqrt{2gY}$$

$$v_1 = \frac{m + M}{m} \sqrt{2gY} \qquad (3)$$

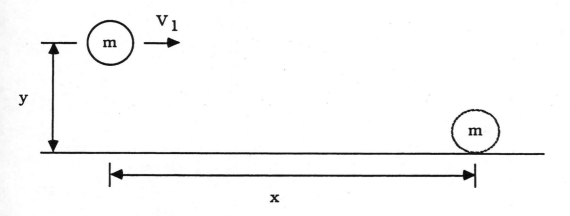

Figure 10.3

In another method used to determine the initial velocity, the ball is projected horizontally and allowed to follow a trajectory to the ground. The equations describing this motion are

$$x(t) = x(0) + v_x(0)\, t + \frac{1}{2} a_x t^2$$

$$y(t) = y(0) + v_y(0)\, t + \frac{1}{2} a_y t^2$$

where

$$x(t) = x \qquad y(t) = 0$$

$$x(0) = 0 \qquad y(0) = y$$

$$v_x(0) = v_1 \quad v_y(0) = 0$$

$$a_x = 0 \quad a_y = -g$$

$$v_1 = \frac{x}{t} \qquad t = \sqrt{\frac{2y}{g}}$$

$$v_1 = \frac{x}{\sqrt{\frac{2y}{g}}} \qquad (4)$$

Thus the initial velocity of the ball can be determined using either the conservation of mechanical energy or the equations of motion.

OPERATION OF THE BALLISTICS PENDULUM

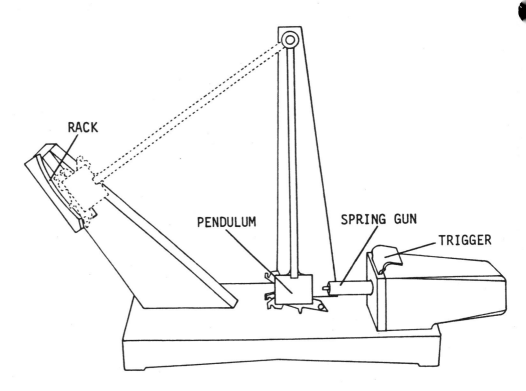

Figure 10.4

The ballistic pendulum apparatus consists of a ballistic pendulum and a spring gun for firing a brass projectile. A single hole drilled through the spherical brass projectile allows it to be mounted on the center rod of the spring gun and the ball is propelled forward when the trigger releases the spring loaded firing rod.

The ballistic pendulum is a massive cylindrical bob suspended by a strong light rod which is pivoted at its upper end. The center of gravity of the pendulum bob lies along the axis of this suspension rod and is indicated by a small red dot. The bob is hollowed out to receive the projectile. A spring catches and holds the brass ball such that the center of gravity of the combined pendulum bob and ball lies along the axis of the suspension rod. Thus the pendulum bob hangs in the same position whether or not it contains the ball.

When the ball is fired and caught by the pendulum bob, the pendulum swings upward and is stopped at its highest point by a pawl that engages a tooth in the curved rack. A scale along the outer edge of the rack can be used to determine the position of the pendulum.

LEARNING OBJECTIVES

After completing the experiment, you should be able to do the following.

1. Define a totally inelastic collision.

2. Set up, and solve an equation for a totally inelastic collision.

3. Recognize that kinetic energy is not conserved in the collision, but after the collision, the remaining kinetic energy is converted into potential energy as the system rises.

4. Recognize that the change in the kinetic energy in the collision is a measure of the work done on the system.

PROCEDURE

A.   DETERMINATION OF THE INITIAL VELOCITY OF THE PROJECTILE

1. Using the double pan balance, measure and record the mass of the brass projectile. Record the mass of the pendulum that is written on the pendulum bob.

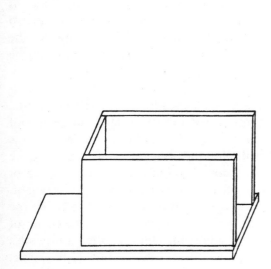
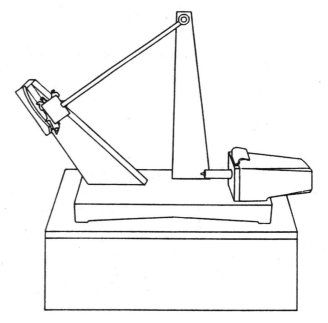

Figure 10.5

2. The initial velocity of the projectile will be determined by firing the ball and allowing it to follow a trajectory to the ground. Place the platform box **on the floor** and set the ballistic pendulum apparatus securely on top of the box. Engage the pawl of the pendulum bob on the rack so that it will not interfere with the free flight of the ball when it is fired.

The target box that will be used to receive the brass ball as it falls to the floor should be placed approximately two meters away from the ballistic pendulum.

Prepare the spring gun for firing by sliding the brass ball onto the center rod of the spring gun. Use it to push the collar on the rod back until a single click is heard, indicating that the trigger is engaged. Since the spring in the gun is compressed by the same amount each time the trigger is engaged, the ball has approximately the same initial speed each time the gun is fired.

3. Fire the ball and note the approximate location of the ball's impact. Place the target box at that position, tape a sheet of white paper on the bottom of the target box and cover it with a piece of carbon paper. When the ball strikes the bottom of the box, a small dot will mark where the ball lands.

Fire the ball six times, making certain that the ballistic pendulum and the target box do not move during this procedure.

4. The vertical height marker will be used to determine the vertical distance, y, traveled by the projectile. It consists of a support rod and two clamps, each holding a small metal pointer that will indicate the initial and the final vertical positions of the projectile. The total vertical displacement of the projectile will then be the distance between the two pointers.

Set one pointer level with the top of the ball when it is still on the center rod of the spring gun. Set the second pointer at the top of the ball when it is placed in the target box. Measure and record the distance between the two pointers. Repeat this procedure to obtain six independent readings for the vertical displacement. Determine the average and standard deviation for the six readings.

5. Use the plumb bob and the 2-meter stick to measure the horizontal range, x, of the ball. While doing this be certain that the target box does not move. Remove the carbon paper from the box and lightly circle the spots representing the impacts of the ball. With the trigger not engaged, place the ball on the center rod of the gun. Loop the plumb bob over one end of the 2-meter stick. Hold the 2-meter stick level so that one end is resting on the brass ball and the opposite end extends over the target box. Slide the plumb bob along the 2-meter stick until it is suspended over the center of the circle containing the impact dots; adjust the length of the plump bob's string until the tip of the plumb bob just touches the center of the circle. Record the position of the pendulum bob and the position of the ball on the spring gun.

6. To determine the experimental uncertainty for x, measure and record the radius of the circle formed by the impact dots.

B. DETERMINATION OF THE VERTICAL RISE OF THE PENDULUM

1. Allow the pendulum to hang freely and at rest. Place the height indicator as close as possible to the pendulum bob when it is at its lowest point. Position one clamp on the support rod such that the pointer is at the same height as the center of gravity of the pendulum bob, indicated by the small red index dot. Clamp the pointer in place and move the height marker to the side, away from the ballistic pendulum.

2. Prepare the spring gun for firing. Release the pendulum from the rack and allow it to hang freely. Once the pendulum is at rest, fire the ball into the pendulum bob by depressing the trigger. Hold the trigger down until the ball has been caught and the pendulum is moving upward. This prevents the trigger from dragging on the propelling collar while the ball is being fired. The pendulum will swing upward and the pawl will engage a tooth on the rack, retaining the pendulum at its highest point.

3. Use the height marker to indicate the vertical position of the pendulum bob after it comes to rest on the rack. Place the marker as close as possible to the pendulum bob and position the second clamp so that the pointer is at the same height as the red index dot at the center of gravity of the pendulum bob.

4. Using the meter stick, measure and record the distance between the two pointers.

5. Repeat procedures 2–6 five more times and calculate the average and standard deviation for the vertical rise of the pendulum bob.

QUESTIONS

1. Taking into account the experimental uncertainties, was momentum conserved for the collision? If it wasn't, explain.

2. Using equations (1), (2), and (3), show that the fractional loss of kinetic energy during the collision is equal to $\dfrac{M}{m + M}$.

3. What became of the kinetic energy that was lost in the collision?

Inelastic Collisions

Name: _____   Lab Section #: _____

Date: _____   Lab Partners: _____

A. DETERMINATION OF THE INITIAL VELOCITY OF THE PROJECTILE

(1) Mass of the pendulum bob _____

   Mass of the brass ball _____

(4) Vertical displacement: y

METER STICK READINGS

	position of top pointer	position of bottom pointer	displacement y
reading 1			
reading 2			
reading 3			
reading 4			
reading 5			
reading 6			

Average = _____

Standard deviation = _____

(5–6) Range: x

position of plumb bomb	position of brass ball	range $x \pm \Delta x$

B. DETERMINATION OF THE VERTICAL RISE OF THE PENDULUM

(4-5) Vertical rise: Y

METER STICK READINGS

	position of top pointer	position of bottom pointer	vertical rise Y
reading 1			
reading 2			
reading 3			
reading 4			
reading 5			
reading 6			

Average = _____

Standard deviation = _____

CALCULATIONS

1. Use equation (4) and the data from part A to compute the magnitude of the initial velocity v_1 of the brass ball. Use the propagation of errors to determine the uncertainty Δv_1.

2. Calculate the magnitude of the velocity V (and ΔV) of the combined pendulum bob and brass ball after the collision using equation (2) and the data from part B.

3. Compute the magnitude of the total momentum of the system before the collision and after the collision (report the experimental uncertainty for each value).

4. Compute the kinetic energy of the system before the collision and after the collision. What fraction of kinetic energy was lost during the collision?

5. Compute the ratio of the mass of the pendulum to the mass of the combined pendulum and ball: $\dfrac{M}{m + M}$. Compare this to the fraction of kinetic energy that was lost.

6. Using equation (3) and the data from part B, compute the magnitude of the initial velocity v_1 of the brass ball (do not forget to determine the uncertainty, Δv_1).

7. Compute the % difference for the two values obtained for v_1 in calculations 1 and 6. Do the two values agree with one another to within the experimental uncertainty?

Centripetal Force

THEORY

Circular motion at constant speed is an accelerated motion. Although the magnitude of the velocity (the speed) remains constant, the direction of the velocity is continually changing and any time the velocity vector changes, there is an accelerating force present. An external force that changes the direction of the velocity of an object so that it travels in a circular path is called a centripetal force, since it is always directed toward the center of the circle of motion. In the absence of this force, the object would resume its linear motion and move away from the center of the circle in a path that is tangent to the circle.

Any type of force (frictional, magnetic, even the tension of a string that is tied to a rotating mass) can act as a centripetal force. The magnitude of this force will be given by

$$F_c = \frac{mv^2}{r} \qquad (1)$$

where v is the linear velocity of the mass, m, moving in a circle of radius, r. The linear velocity is just the distance traveled per unit time. For instance, every time the mass completes one revolution, it travels a distance $2\pi r$ and the velocity is

$$v = \frac{2\pi r}{T}, \qquad (2)$$

where T is the period or the time it takes to make one revolution. We can also express the velocity in terms of the frequency, which is the inverse of the period (or the number of revolutions per unit time).

$$v = 2\pi r f, \qquad (3)$$

where f is the frequency. Altogether, we have for the centripetal force:

$$F_c = 4\pi^2 f^2 mr. \qquad (4)$$

Our purpose in this experiment is to study the centripetal force given by Equation 4. The apparatus we will use is shown in Figure 11.1. When the plastic tube is swung in a small circle above your head, the racket ball moves around in a horizontal circle at the end of a string which is threaded through the tube and fastened to one of the hooked masses hanging below. The force

Purpose

To determine the relationship between the centripetal force and the frequency of rotation.

Apparatus

Racket ball with string and alligator clip attached, plastic tube, hooked mass set, balance, stopwatch, and safety goggles.

of gravity on the hooked mass, acting along the string, provides the horizontal force needed to keep the racket ball moving in a circle. This horizontal force is the centripetal force.

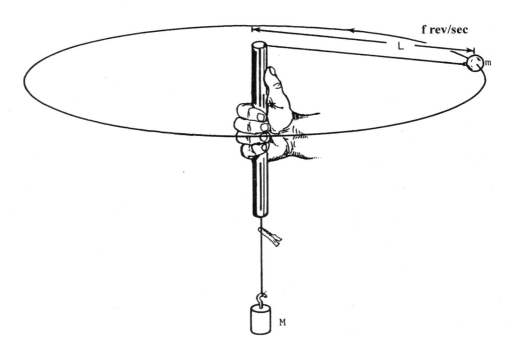

Figure 11.1

You will notice that as you whirl the racket ball around, the part of the string from the tube to the racket ball was not quite horizontal. The gravitational force acting on the racket ball pulls it down.

We can understand the combined effects of gravitational force and centripetal force on the ball by looking at Figure 11.2. Here we see a schematic side view of the apparatus shown in Figure 11.1. The distance, r, is the distance from the center of gravity of the ball to the axis about which the ball rotates. θ is the angle between r and the string. L is the distance from the center of gravity of the ball to the intersection of the string with the axis of rotation. Note that in Figure 2

$$r/L = \cos \theta. \qquad (5)$$

We can also see that the force exerted by the string on the ball has two components, F_g and F_c. F_g is the force necessary to balance the weight W (mg) so that there is no vertical motion. Since $F_g = W$, there is no net motion in the vertical axis. F_c is the centripetal force required to keep the ball moving in a circle. This is the force that is directed towards the center of the circle of motion and keeps the mass on a circular path. Note that

$$F_c/F_{string} = \cos \theta \qquad (6)$$

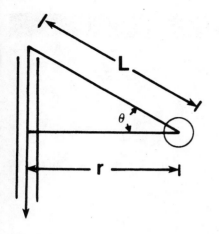 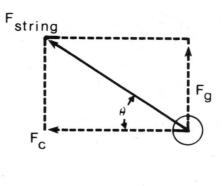

Figure 11.2

From Equation 6, we have

$$F_{string} = \frac{F_c}{\cos\theta} \qquad (7)$$

Replacing F_c by its expression in Equation 2, Equation 7 becomes

$$F_{string} = \frac{4\pi^2 f^2 mr}{\cos\theta} \qquad (8)$$

Next, if $\cos\theta$ is replaced in Equation 8 by its expression in Equation 5, Equation 8 becomes,

$$F_{string} = 4\pi^2 f^2\, mL. \qquad (9)$$

The force or tension on the string is provided by the weight of the hooked mass, Mg, at the end of the string, so

$$F_{string} = Mg. \qquad (10)$$

Finally, F_{string} in Equation 9 is replaced by its expression in Equation 8 so that Equation 9 becomes

$$Mg = 4\pi^2 f^2\, mL$$

or,

$$M/L = (4\pi^2 m/g)f^2. \qquad (11)$$

After completing the experiment, you should be able to do the following:

1. State the conditions for uniform circular motion.

2. Show all forms for uniform circular motion are dimensionally correct.

3. Show with a free body diagram, the forces acting on a body undergoing uniform circular motion.

4. Relate period of rotation to frequency of motion.

5. Know that centripetal force is a force causing a change in the direction not in the speed of a body.

6. Know that centripetal force and centripetal acceleration are parallel to the radius of the circular path while velocity is tangent to it.

PROCEDURE

1. Place a hooked mass of 100 gm at the end of the string and whirl the racket ball over your head while holding on to the string below the tube. Practice spinning the ball over your head while maintaining the path of the ball completely horizontal, until you can let go of the string below the tube and maintain the same motion. Now increase the speed of the ball (whirl it faster) and note if you must increase or decrease the tension (hooked mass on the end of the string) to keep the same horizontal path and radius. Each lab partner should do this exercise. (Wear safety goggles!)

2. To start the first part of the experiment, pull enough string through the tube so that the length, L, (the radius of the tube plus the distance from the top edge of the tube to the center of gravity of the ball, see Figure 1) is about 50 cm. Attach an alligator clip to the string about 1 cm (ΔL) below the plastic tube to serve as a marker so that you can keep the radius constant while whirling the ball. Measure and record L and ΔL to one decimal place accuracy in cm.

3. Once L_1 is determined, hang a 100 gm hooked mass, M_1, at the end of the string. Now swing the ball over your head maintaining a constant speed and radius (the alligator clip should be motionless). While you do this, your lab partner will measure the time it takes the ball to swing through a fixed number (such as 30) revolutions. Record the initial time on the stopwatch and the final time (after the 30 revolutions). Subtract to obtain the total time. Repeat this procedure a second time. If your second total time differs from your first total time by more than 2 seconds, you must repeat the procedure until you obtain two time estimates that differ by no more than 2 seconds.

4. Now place a hooked mass, M_2, at the end of the string that is less than 100 gm and more than 50 gm. Without changing the length, L, or the position of the alligator clip, repeat step 3. Record M_2 and the total times.

5. Next place a hooked mass, M_3, that is more than 100 gms but less than 300 gms at the end of the string. Without changing the length, L, or the position of the alligator clip, repeat step 3. Record M_3 and the total times.

6. Now change the length, L, so that it is between 30 and 50 cm. Measure and record L_4 to one decimal place in cm. Place a 100 gm hooked mass, M_4, at the end of the string. Repeat step 3.

7. Finally, change the length, L, so that it is between 50 and 70 cm. Measure and record L_5 to one decimal place in cm. Place a 100 gm hooked mass, M_5, at the end of the string. Repeat step 3.

8. Determine the mass, m, of the ball.

Centripetal Force

Name: _____   Lab Section #: _____

Date: _____   Lab Partners: _____

I. DATA

$L_1 = ($ _____ $\pm .5) - ($ _____ $\pm .5)$ cm = _____ ± 1.0 cm $= L_2 = L_3$

$M_1 = 100$ gm $t_f =$ _____ sec $t_1 =$ _____ sec $t_1 = t_f - t_i =$ _____ sec

$t_f =$ _____ sec $t_i =$ _____ sec $t_2 =$ _____ sec

$M_2 =$ _____ gm $t_f =$ _____ sec $t_i =$ _____ sec $t_1 =$ _____ sec

$t_f =$ _____ sec $t_i =$ _____ sec $t_2 =$ _____ sec

$M_3 =$ _____ gm $t_f =$ _____ sec $t_i =$ _____ sec $t_1 =$ _____ sec

$t_f =$ _____ sec $t_i =$ _____ sec $t_2 =$ _____ sec

$L_4 = ($ _____ $\pm .5) - ($ _____ $\pm .5)$ cm = _____ ± 1.0 cm

$M_4 = 100$ gm $t_f =$ _____ sec $t_i =$ _____ sec $t_1 = t_f - t_i =$ _____ sec

$t_f =$ _____ sec $t_i =$ _____ sec $t_2 =$ _____ sec

$L_5 = ($ _____ $\pm .5) - ($ _____ $\pm .5)$ cm = _____ ± 1.0 cm

$M_5 = 100$ gm $t_f =$ _____ sec $t_i =$ _____ sec $t_1 = t_f - t_i =$ _____ sec

$t_f =$ _____ sec $t_i =$ _____ sec $t_2 =$ _____ sec

mass of ball = _____ gm

No. of revolutions _____

(A) For each of your five values of M and L, calculate the following and show a sample calculation of each below.

$$f_1 = \frac{\text{number of rev}}{t_1} \qquad f_2 = \frac{\text{number of rev}}{t_2} \qquad f = \frac{f_1 + f_2}{2} \qquad \Delta f = |\frac{f_1 - f_2}{2}|$$

	$f_1\left(\dfrac{1}{\text{sec}}\right)$	$f_2(1/\text{sec})$	$f(1/\text{sec})$	$\Delta f(1/\text{sec})$
1.				
2.				
3.				
4.				
5.				

(B) For each value of M, L, f and Δf, calculate the following and show a sample calculation of each below.

$$\Delta \frac{M}{L} = \frac{M}{L}\left[\frac{\Delta L}{L}\right] \qquad\qquad \Delta f^2 = f^2\frac{2\Delta f}{f} = f\,2\Delta f$$

	$\dfrac{M}{L}\ \dfrac{g}{cm}$		$\dfrac{\Delta M}{L}\ \dfrac{g}{cm}$	f^2 (1/sec^2)	Δf^2 (1/sec^2)
1.					
2.					
3.					
4.					

(C) Plot $\dfrac{M}{L}$ vs. f^2. Find the slope of the line. Show your work on the graph, including the *units* of the slope.

(D) Compute $\dfrac{4\pi^2 m}{g}$ and compare this to your slope by obtaining a percent error.

Vibratory Motion of a Spring

THEORY

Elasticity is that property of a body that causes it to return to its original shape and size after being distorted by a force. This distorting force will be supplied by the mass we add to the pan.

$$F_{applied} = mg \tag{1}$$

The elongation of the spring is directly proportional to the force applied, provided that the elastic limit is not exceeded. By Newton's third law, an elastic restoring force is produced in the spring. The elastic restoring force is directed to the equilibrium position and therefore is *opposite* to the displacement and can be expressed as

$$F = -kx \tag{2}$$

Where x is the elongation of the spring, F is the force applied to the spring, and k is a constant of proportionality which depends on the size and shape of the spring, as well as its elastic properties. This relationship is known as Hooke's law.

Such a restoring force is characteristic of simple harmonic motion. So a mass suspended from the lower end of the spring will vibrate with simple harmonic motion if it is displaced a small distance and then released.

The period T for this motion is given by

$$T = 2\pi\sqrt{-\frac{x}{a}} \tag{3}$$

x is the displacement from the equilibrium position, a is the acceleration (note that a is opposite in direction to x) so $-\dfrac{x}{a}$ is a positive number.

Starting with equation (3), we may derive an expression for the period in terms of the mass and the spring constant, k.

Given that F = −kx, and F = ma, we can equate the equations and write

$$\frac{m}{k} = \frac{-x}{a} \tag{4}$$

Purpose

To verify the laws of simple harmonic motion for the spring.

Apparatus

Hooke's Law apparatus, which includes a spring, mass holder with pointer and a scale, slotted masses and a timer.

Substituting equation (4) into (3), we have

$$T = 2\pi\sqrt{\frac{m}{k}} \tag{5}$$

Here m is the effective mass that is equal to the sum of the suspended mass, the mass of the pan, and one-third mass of the spring since not all the mass of the spring takes part in the vibration of the spring.

LEARNING OBJECTIVES

After completing this experiment you should be able to do the following:

1. Define and give an example of an object undergoing periodic motion.

2. State why elastic materials behave as if they have a memory.

3. Explain and demonstrate how to determine the spring constant for a given spring.

4. State the relationship between the mass undergoing periodic motion and the spring constant of the mass-spring system.

5. Be able to correctly show the unit conversion:

$$s = \left(\frac{kg \cdot m}{N}\right)^{\frac{1}{2}}$$

6. Be able to obtain information from the intercept of a graph.

PROCEDURE

1. Determine the force constant of the spring by adding masses to the spring, one at a time. Since there is a variance in both the spring and the Hooke's Law apparatus used in this experiment, your instructor will tell you the maximum mass that should be used in your setup and the mass increments to be used. There should be at least six mass increments. Unload the spring, one mass at a time, and note the elongation. Is this an elastic spring? Plot a graph of force vs. elongation and take the slope of the line. Is this value a force constant?

2. Determine the time for one complete vertical oscillation. We call this the period, T. To do this, attach the first known mass and pull the spring slightly from down its equilibrium position and release it. The system is now oscillating. Record the time for 50 complete oscillations and then determine the period. Repeat with the same mass increments you used in procedure 1.

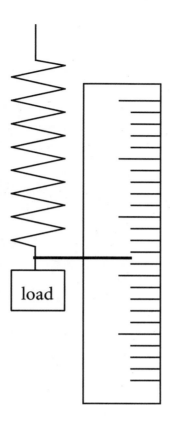

Figure 12.1

3. Theory suggests the period, T, is related to the spring constant, k, by equation (5). Plot a graph of T^2 vs. mass $_{effective}$. Determine the value of k from the graph and compare it to the value of k that you determined in procedure 1.

4. Attach an unknown mass to the spring and pull it slightly downward from the equilibrium position and let it vibrate. Record the total time for 50 oscillations and find the period. Determine the unknown mass. Compare this mass to the value obtained from a laboratory balance.

QUESTIONS

1. Does the plot of force versus elongation indicate that the spring obeys Hooke's Law? Why or why not?

2. What would happen if the elastic limit of the spring were exceeded?

3. Why is one-third of the mass of the spring used in calculating the period rather than all of the mass?

4. Calculate the work required to elongate the spring by 10 cm.

Vibratory Motion of a Spring

Name: _____   Date: _____

Increment	Mass m	Applied force	Elongation x loading	Elongation x unloading
No.	kg	N	m	m
1				
2				
3				
4				
5				
6				

Mass pan _____

Mass spring _____

Trial	Effective mass m	Time for 50 vibrations	Period T	Period T squared
No.	kg	s	s	s^2
1				
2				
3				
4				
5				
6				

The Simple Pendulum

THEORY

In the world of nature we often find processes and events which periodically repeat themselves in time. By this we mean that after a certain time interval, or period, the system or process returns to its initial condition. The tides in the ocean, the positions of the sun, moon, and planets and lunar eclipses, and a host of other astronomical phenomena recur with a more or less complicated regularity. Early man was certainly aware of this recurrence, and it had a religious significance for him. Numerous temples, such as the impressive Stonehenge monument in England, were constructed with astronomical recurrence as their central theme. These ancient ideas still exert a subtle influence today where we find them in religion, art, and even historical theory.

But these examples of periodicity are all quite complex and we would be hard pressed to extract any manageable data from them. However, there are a number of examples in which the situation is quite simple, with certain events and processes occurring with strict and simple regularity. One such example is a mass swinging on the end of a string. If the magnitude of the displacement is sufficiently small, and if we neglect the effects of friction and air resistance, the motion of the mass is exceptionally simple and is called *simple harmonic motion*. Problems of this type, and their mathematical equivalents, are found throughout the whole of physics and engineering.

Let us examine the above example more closely. A simplified pendulum consists of a mass M suspended by a very long light string of length L from a support, as in Fig. 13.1a. If we allow the mass to move in one plane only, we have what is known as the *simple pendulum*, a device famous for its use in the grandfather clock. The mass m is called the bob of the pendulum. At time t = 0 we displace the mass a distance R to the right, as measure from the vertical or equilibrium position, and then release it. Consider the forces acting upon m just after it is released. There is the weight, w = mg, pulling downward and the tension T in the string, as shown in Fig. 13.1b. A careful analysis shows that there is a net force acting to move the mass back to its original position. The restoring force F is proportional to the displacement, so long as the displacement is small, and it always points in the direction of the equilibrium position. Since there is an unbalanced force acting on m, Newton's second law tells us that the object will be accelerated in the direction of F

Purpose

To study a simple pendulum and the factors that determine the period of the pendulum, and to determine the acceleration due to gravity.

Apparatus

Metal sphere, long string, vernier caliper, stopwatch, meterstick, and pendulum clamp and support.

Source: Puri
Modified by Zober and Zober

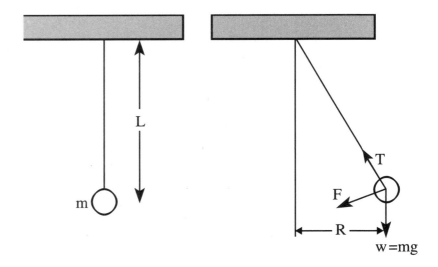

Figure 13.1a   **Figure 13.1b**

The bob thus returns to the equilibrium position, but when it arrives there it has a velocity. Inertia then carries the bob beyond the equilibrium position, but the restoring force F is now reversed in direction and decelerates the bob. Eventually the velocity of the bob becomes zero, but it is now displaced a distance R to the left of the equilibrium position (ignoring the force of friction). This process repeats and the bob is returned to its original position. The time required for this complete cycle of motion is called the *period*.

An immediate question concerning the simple pendulum is: "Upon what does the period depend?" If we are performing a pendulum experiment in the laboratory, we might make a list of the things that could influence the period. By this we mean that a change in one of these items on the list would cause some change in the period of the pendulum. Our list might include such diverse items as the size and shape of the laboratory room, the temperature, or the color of the dress or shirt worn by the experimenter, as well as more obvious quantities such as the mass of the bob, the displacement, and the length of the string. First, we can reduce the size of our list by using our intuition. One feels that many factors such as the color of the eyes of the experimenter or where the moon is relative to the constellation Sagittarius are irrelevant to the experiment. Second, we can reduce the list further by making "Inspired guesses." Good science is as much a product of intuition and inspiration as are good literature and good music. For example, we might guess that the temperature has no effect upon the period of the pendulum even though we have no reason for doing so.

Once we have decided which factors are to remain in the list, we proceed to the laboratory to test our ideas. If some important item has been omitted, it will be decided experimentally, either by us or by other experimenters who try to reproduce our work under different circumstances. In checking the effects of varying different variables, it is necessary to vary only one at a time, otherwise the response is inconclusive. These points will be further illustrated in the experiment itself.

After completing this experiment you should be able to do the following:

1. Show the relationship between period and frequency.

2. Understand that motion of the pendulum is harmonic motion but not simple harmonic motion and be able to explain why.

3. Determine the factors that will affect the motion of a pendulum.

4. Show that the equation used in procedure 6 is dimensionally correct.

5. Understand that the length and period of a pendulum are related to the acceleration due to gravity.

PROCEDURE

PART A.

1. Set the pendulum length to 20.0 cm. The distance from the pendulum clamp to the center of the bob is the length, L.

2. Using trigonometry, calculate the displacement the bob would have to give it a displacement of 5°. Displace the bob to the right that amount, starting your stopwatch at the moment the bob is released.

3. Allow the bob to move through fifty (50) complete cycles and stop the watch at the end of the 50th cycle.

4. Divide your time by 50 to determine the time of one swing that gives the period of the pendulum.

5. Square the period and record in your data.

6. The period of a pendulum can be found from $T = 2\pi\sqrt{\frac{L}{g}}$. Use this equation and calculate the acceleration due to gravity.

7. Repeat the procedures for lengths of 40.0 cm, 50.0 cm, 60.0 cm, 80.0 cm, and 100.0 cm.

8. Plot a graph of the period as a function of the length. By studying this graph, see if you can find a way to plot the data to give a straight line. Hint: You might plot T vs. $\frac{1}{L}$ or T vs. L^2. From your studies, how does the period depend upon the length?

Part B.

Next, you should investigate the influence of the mass on the period by varying the mass of the bob. Again, be sure that you carefully describe what you did, what results you obtained, and your conclusions. Discuss how this result could be expected from Newton's second law and the law of gravitation.

Part C.

Finally, does the horizontal displacement have any effect upon the period? Check it experimentally and describe your results. Be sure to state what variables you held constant, which bob you used, etc.

Questions

1. A boy and a girl start swinging in similar swings at the same time. The boy weighs more than the girl. The boy is more energetic and soon he is swinging higher than the girl. Which one will complete more swings in the same time interval. Explain.

2. Theoretical studies of the simple pendulum have shown that this period T is given by $T = 2\pi\sqrt{\frac{L}{g}}$, where g is the acceleration due to gravity. From your second graph, find the value of g. There you plotted T^2 vs. L. If we square the equation for the period, we obtain $T^2 = \frac{4\pi^2}{g}L$. Therefore, the slope of the graph is $\frac{4\pi^2}{g}$. Measure this slope and find g. Compare your results with the value given in some handbook.

3. Give another example of periodic motion other than simple harmonic motion.

4. If you landed on the moon, could you use the pendulum method to find the acceleration due to gravity for the surface of the moon? Explain.

5. Why must the angle through which the pendulum swings be not more than 5 degrees?

6. The actual length of the simple pendulum is from the point of suspension to the center of oscillation. How would measuring the length of the pendulum from the point of suspension to the bob alter your outcome?

7. From the graph T^2 vs. L, find what length pendulum must be to beat seconds (Periodic time = 2 s). The grandfather clock often uses such pendulums.

8. Explain why it was not necessary to measure the mass of the each bob.

The Simple Pendulum

Name: _____   Date: _____

Diameter of bob _____

Radius of bob _____

Accepted value of g $= 9.80\frac{m}{s^2}$

PART A: THE EFFECT OF LENGTH ON THE PERIOD

Heavy bob, displacement = 5° are held constant.

Pendulum length	Number of swings	Total time of 50 swings	Period	Period squared	Acceleration due to gravity
L	N	t	T	T²	g
cm	—	s	s	s²	$\frac{m}{s^2}$

PART B: THE EFFECT OF ANGULAR DISPLACEMENT ON THE PERIOD

Heavy bob, length = 100 cm are held constant.

Displacement	5°	15°	20°
time for 50 swings			
time for 1 swing			

PART C: THE EFFECT OF MASS ON PERIOD

Length = 100 cm, displacement = 5° are held constant.

Mass	heavy	light
time for 50 swings		
time for 1 swing		

Boyle's Law

THEORY

Boyle's law for an ideal gas is an isothermal process, the temperature of the mass of a confined gas remains constant, thus the volume of the gas varies as the inverse of the pressure.

The ideal gas equation is given by

$$PV = nRT \qquad (1)$$

where nRT is a constant, and,

$$P_1 V_1 = K \qquad (2)$$

$$P_2 V_2 = K \qquad (3)$$

Then,

$$P_1 V_1 = P_2 V_2 \qquad (4)$$

The gauge pressure acting on the gas trapped in the syringe is determined by dividing the force applied to the harness on the plunger divided by the area of the plunger.

$$P = \frac{F}{A} \qquad (5)$$

Boyle's law requires that the pressure is measured in absolute terms, thus we must add atmospheric pressure to the gauge pressure.

$$P_{absolute} = P_{gauge} + P_{atmospheric} \qquad (6)$$

Purpose

To verify Boyle's Law.

Apparatus

Boyle's Law apparatus—syringe form, masses, mass hanger, and Vernier caliper, thermometer.

LEARNING OBJECTIVES

After completing this lab you will be able to do the following:

1. Calculate the pressure acting on the system.

2. Explain the difference between gauge pressure and absolute pressure and be able to convert from one to the other.

3. Show the product of PV has units of joules.

4. Explain the significance of the PV column on your data sheet.

5. Explain the shape of the V vs. P graph and $\frac{1}{V}$ vs. P graph.

PROCEDURE

1. Using the Vernier, measure and record the diameter of the plunger of the syringe in cm. Convert this reading to SI units and record. Do not compress the sides of the plunger as you obtain the reading.

2. Calculate and record the area of the plunger in m^2.

3. Record the atmospheric pressure in the room and the room temperature.

4. Trap air in the cylinder and record the initial volume reading in m^3.

5. Place a mass on the apparatus. After the plunger has stopped moving determine the new volume. Record both the mass and the new volume. When you make your readings do not handle the barrel of the syringe; you do not want to transfer heat energy from your hands into the system.

6. Repeat procedure 5 by adding an additional mass. Do not hurry through your readings. Let the system adjust before adding additional masses.

7. Continue adding masses until you have taken at least eight readings of mass and volume.

8. Calculate the force, the gauge pressure, and the absolute pressure for each reading and record.

9. Calculate the reciprocal of the volume in m^{-3} for each reading and record.

10. Calculate PV for each reading and record.

11. Plot graphs of V vs. P and $\dfrac{1}{V}$ vs. P.

QUESTIONS

1. What is the shape of the curve in each case?

2. Is the product PV a constant? What might have affected your readings?

3. Does Boyle's law hold for any temperature? For any pressure?

4. Determine the number of moles of air trapped in the syringe.

Boyle's Law

Name: _____   Date: _____

Diameter of plunger _____   Room temperature _____

Area of plunger _____   Atmospheric pressure _____

Trial	Mass m	Force F	Gauge Pressure $\frac{F}{A}$	Absolute pressure	Volume V	$\frac{1}{V}$	PV
No.	kg	N	Pa	Pa	m^3	m^{-3}	J
1							
2							
3							
4							
5							
6							
7							
8							

Linear and Volumetric Expansion of Solids

THEORY

When thermal energy is added to a substance, its dimensions will change. In most cases, it will expand. (Water is an exception—in the range of 0°C to 4°C it will contract.) Experiments have shown that the change is directly proportional to the amount of material. A rod 1 m long will expand 10 times more than a rod 10 m long. This expansion is also directly proportional to the temperature change. The change in length of the substance is given by:

$$\Delta L = L_o \alpha (t_f - t_i) \qquad (1)$$

The coefficient, α for a given material, is expressed as a fractional change in length per C°. This coefficient varies slightly with temperature, but if the change in the temperature is not too great, we can ignore it. ΔL is only accurate if it is small in comparison to L_o.

Thermal energy added to a material will produce a change in all dimensions. A plate with an initial area A_o will increase in area. If the plate's properties are the same in both directions, the dimensions will increase in length by equation (1). We can express the area change as:

$$A = LW$$

where $L = \Delta L + L_o$ and $W = \Delta W + W_o$

$$then\ A = A_o(1 + \alpha \Delta t)^2$$

$$A = A_o(1 + 2\alpha \Delta t + (\alpha \Delta t)^2)$$

The coefficient of linear expansion has values of $\dfrac{10^{-6}}{C°}$, therefore $(\alpha \Delta t)^2$ can be neglected.

The area equation reduces to $A = A_o(1 + 2\alpha \Delta t)$, thus

$$\Delta A = A_o \gamma \Delta t \ \text{where}\ \gamma = 2\alpha \qquad (2)$$

(If there is a hole in the plate, the hole will act like the material surrounding it and expand at the same rate.)

Source: Puri
Modified by Zober and Zober

Purpose

To determine the coefficients of (a) linear expansion and (b) volumetric expansion of a solid.

Apparatus

Linear expansion apparatus, steam generator, burner or hot plate, rubber tubing, thermometers, volumetric expansion apparatus, various rods and liquids.

The volumetric change for a solid can be expressed as

$$\Delta V_o \beta \Delta t \quad \text{where} \quad \beta = 3\alpha \tag{3}$$

Again the material must be isotropic—that is having the same properties in all directions. Liquids and gases have no fixed shapes and do not undergo linear expansion. The change in the volume of a liquid can be expressed by equation (3). However, β for a gas varies greatly with temperature. We will deal with expansion of a gas from the gas law equations.

LEARNING OBJECTIVES

After completing this experiment you should be able to do the following:

1. Relate the coefficient of expansion to the number of dimensions undergoing a change.

2. Be able to write and solve an equation for a linear, area, or volumetric expansion of a solid.

3. Be able to write and solve an equation for the volumetric expansion of a liquid.

4. Be able to write and solve an equation for the net expansion for a liquid contained in a solid material.

PROCEDURE

PART A. LINEAR EXPANSION

1. Measure the length of a rod, recording both the original length and the type of material.

2. Insert the rod into the hollow metal jacket, capping the ends with two rubber stoppers (one hole). Make sure that the ends of the rod extend to the outer surface of the stoppers.

3. One end of the rod must be in contact with the fixed end of the apparatus. The other end is to be in contact with the micrometer screw. This screw will engage a dial indicator (the scale is in mm). Adjust the screw so that the indicator reads zero. Do this by making the scale reading slightly larger than zero and then backing it off to zero. Tighten the clamps holding the tube in the jacket. Insert the thermometer, read the initial temperature and record.

4. Attach the steam hose to one end of the apparatus, make sure that the outlet hose is in a beaker. Record the temperature when the rod has stopped expanding. Record the reading on the indicator.

5. Disconnect the steam hose. Cool the metal jacket and remove the rod. Reassemble the system with a new rod and repeat the procedure.

6. Make determinations of the linear expansion for at least four different materials.

7. Solve for the linear expansion of each material. Compare it with the standard for the material.

PART B. VOLUMETRIC EXPANSION

1. Fill the glass bulb with a liquid to the zero mark or slightly above. Generally the bulb will have a capacity in ml marked on the bulb (most often 10 ml or 25 ml). Record both the initial volume of the liquid and the liquid used. The capillary stem has a capacity of 0.5 ml and is graduated to 0.01 ml.

2. Place the glass bulb in the water bath. Adjust the position of the bulb and the thermometer to prevent them from resting on the bottom of the beaker. Add water at room temperature to the beaker. Make sure that it just covers the bulb, but not the stem of the expansion tube. Record the temperature— if there is a change in volume record the new reading as V_o.

3. Turn on the heating element (low setting) and begin the experiment, stirring the water bath gently. Record the temperature and the volume in the stem for at least eight data values. Stop recording when the liquid has reached the last mark on the stem. (You may have to cool the system and start again, if you heated it too quickly.)

4. Repeat with two additional liquids.

5. Plot a graph of ΔV vs. temperature. What type of line results? Take the slope of the line. The slope divided by V_o gives the apparent coefficient of cubical expansion. To obtain the true value for the liquid, you must add the coefficient of cubical expansion for the glass. Why?

6. Determine the absolute error and the percent error for each liquid.

QUESTIONS

1. What would happen if the glass of a thermometer had a larger coefficient of cubical expansion than the liquid inside?

2. The thermometer you used in the metal jacket is an immersion type thermometer. Does any correction have to be made since it was in contact with the metal rather than in the steam?

3. What errors, if any, will occur if the steel jacket is not cooled to room temperature before a rod is inserted?

Linear and Volumetric Expansion of Solids

Name: _____   Date: _____

Material	L_o	ΔL	t_i	t_f	Coefficient of expansion
—	cm	cm	°C	°C	$(C°)^{-1}$

PART A: EXPANSION OF A SOLID

PART B: EXPANSION OF LIQUIDS.

Liquid 1 _____

Initial volume, V_o _____   Initial temperature, t_i _____

Trial	ΔV in stem	Temperature t
No.	mL	°C
1		
2		
3		
4		
5		
6		
7		
8		

Liquid 2 _____

Initial volume, V_o _____   Initial temperature, t_i _____

Trial	ΔV in stem	Temperature t
No.	mL	°C
1		
2		
3		
4		
5		
6		
7		
8		

Liquid 3 _____

Initial volume, V_o _____   Initial temperature, t_i _____

Trial No.	ΔV in stem mL	Temperature t °C
1		
2		
3		
4		
5		
6		
7		
8		

Specific Heat

THEORY

The *heat capacity* of a substance is the amount of heat required to raise the temperature of the substance by one degree. In the SI system, the heat capacity is expressed as $\frac{J}{K}$. We may also express the value as $\frac{J}{C^o}$ since the size of a Kelvin is the same size as a Celsius degree.

The *specific heat* of a substance is the ratio of the heat capacity of the substance to a unit mass of the substance. The specific heat, c, is given by:

$$c = \frac{Q}{m \cdot \Delta t} \tag{1}$$

and has units of $\frac{J}{Kg \cdot K}$ or $\frac{J}{Kg \cdot C^o}$. (Older units of $\frac{cal}{g \cdot C^o}$ are sometimes used since the masses of the substances involved are small.) We treat the specific heat capacity of a substance as a constant, but actually it is temperature dependent. However, in the temperature range of this experiment they are fairly consistent.

The experimental determination of the specific heat of a solid by the method of mixtures is a statement of conservation of energy, as long as radiation losses are minimized.

$$Q_{lost} = Q_{gained} \tag{2}$$

The heat energy lost by the sample at some high temperature is transferred to the calorimeter, stirrer and the liquid in the calorimeter that is initially at some lower temperature. Using equation (3) the specific heat of the sample may be determined.

$$mc_{sample}(t_o - t_f) = mc_{cal}(t_f - t_i) + mc_{water}(t_f - t_i) \tag{3}$$

If the stirrer is made of a different material than the calorimeter, a heat term must be added for it.

Purpose

To determine the specific heat of a solid using the method of mixtures.

Apparatus

Calorimeter, samples to be tested, two thermometers, balance and masses, steam generator, and burner.

After completing this experiment you should be able to do the following:

1. Define specific heat capacity.

2. Set up and solve a heat loss equals heat gain equation.

3. Show the conversion between the units of $\dfrac{J}{kg \cdot C^o}$ and $\dfrac{cal}{g \cdot C^o}$.

4. Know that at equilibrium, all parts of the system have the same temperature.

5. Know the direction of energy flow is from the body with the higher temperature to the body with the lower temperature.

PROCEDURE

Part of this experiment is to design your own data sheets. Study the procedures to decide how you will do these data sheets.

1. Mass the sample and record both the mass and the type of material used. Place the sample into the cup of the steam generator and heat the sample until its temperature is at least 95°C. (Do not use the thermometer as a stirrer.)

2. Mass the inner cup of the calorimeter and the stirrer and record their masses. If the stirrer is made from a different material than the calorimeter, mass them separately and record the mass of each. Also record the material of the calorimeter and the stirrer.

3. Fill the inner cup of the calorimeter halfway with water that is at least 5° C below room temperature. Mass the calorimeter cup, stirrer, and water and determine the mass of water present in the calorimeter cup.

4. Place the calorimeter cup into the outer container. Make sure the fiber ring is in place. Cover the calorimeter and determine the initial temperature of the calorimeter-water system. Record this temperature.

5. When the sample's temperature has reached 95° C, remove it and quickly transfer it to the calorimeter. Record the equilibrium temperature for the system.

6. Repeat the experiment with additional samples.

7. Compute the specific heat of the sample and compare this value with the accepted value. Determine the absolute and relative errors.

QUESTIONS

1. Why was the water in the calorimeter taken with an initial temperature below room temperature?

2. Could the specific heat of the metal specimen in this experiment be determined by cooling the metal in an ice-water bath rather than by heating it? Explain.

3. Account for the errors in this experiment.

4. Water has a very high specific heat. Does this influence the climate of cities near oceans?

Change of Phase–Heat of Fusion and Heat of Vaporization

THEORY

Matter exists in solid, liquid, and gaseous forms at normal temperature and pressure ranges.

In the solid phase, thermal energy that is added to the substance will increase the temperature. In dealing with the internal energy of the particles (on the microscopic level we refer to atoms, molecules and ions as particles since their behavior is the same) the thermal energy added will increase the kinetic energy. In Fig. 17.1 the *steepness* of the slope of the line (a) depends on the specific heat of the substance.

Purpose

To determine the heats of fusion and vaporization of water.

Apparatus

Calorimeter and stirrer, steam generator, burner or hot plate, rubber tubing, balance and masses, thermometers, water, and ice.

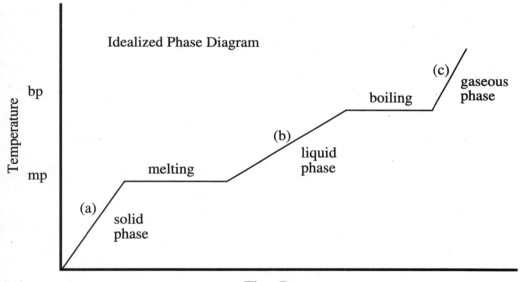

Figure 17.1

At some point, the substance will be heated to its melting point (this is pressure dependent) and additional thermal energy goes into the substance as potential energy and bonds holding the particles in the lattice structure are overcome. No change in temperature will occur until the entire solid is converted into a liquid. At this point additional thermal energy will increase the temperature of the liquid. Note the slope of the line (b) is different because the specific heat in each phase is different. The temperature will continue to increase until the liquid has reached the boiling point temperature (again pressure dependent). At this point, additional energy will free the particles with relatively large separation between them. Since the energy added is in the form of potential energy, no temperature change will occur until all of the liquid has been converted into a vapor. At this point, the temperature will rise since the energy form is kinetic. The slope of line (c) has a different value since it has a different specific heat.

The substance absorbs heat in a transition from solid to liquid and will release the same amount of heat when it solidifies regardless of the temperature at which this transition occurs. This is also true for the liquid-vapor transition, but the energy involved is much greater.

For water, at one atmosphere of pressure, the normal transition temperatures are 273 K (0°C) and 373 K (100°C).

The transition term for fusion is:

$$Q = \pm\, mL_f \tag{1}$$

The latent heat L_f for H_2O is $333.7\dfrac{kJ}{kg}$ or $79.7\dfrac{cal}{g}$

The term for vaporization is given by

$$Q = \pm\, mL_v \tag{2}$$

The latent heat L_v for H_2O is $2259\dfrac{kJ}{kg}$ or $539\dfrac{cal}{g}$

The method of mixtures will be used to determine the latent heats for both transitions. For ice,

$$mc_{cal}(t_i - t_f) + mc_{water}(t_i - t_f) = m_{ice}L_f + mc_{icewater}(t_f - t_o) \tag{3}$$

For steam,

$$m_{steam}L_v + mc_{hotwater}(t_o - t_f) = mc_{coldwater}(t_f - t_i) + mc_{cal}(t_f - t_i) \tag{4}$$

LEARNING OBJECTIVES

After completing this experiment you should be able to do the following:

1. Define the terms—*latent heat of fusion* and *latent heat of vaporization*.

2. Convert from $\dfrac{kJ}{kg}$ to $\dfrac{cal}{g}$.

3. Write a correct phase change equation and solve this equation for the unknown parameter.

4. Be able to explain the phase change diagram in terms of energy added or removed from a substance.

PROCEDURE

PART A.

1. Mass the inner cup of the calorimeter and the stirrer. Record the material and the mass of each. If they are different materials, mass them separately.

2. Add water that is at least 10° C above room temperature to the inner cup of the calorimeter, filling it half way. Mass the calorimeter and water. Record the mass of the water in the cup.

3. Assemble the calorimeter. After you have covered the calorimeter, insert the thermometer and record the temperature of the system.

4. Add a few pieces of well-dried ice to the calorimeter cup. Cover and stir until all of the ice has melted and an equilibrium temperature has been obtained. Record this temperature.

5. Re-mass the system and determine the mass of ice that was added.

6. Write the heat loss equal heat gain equations and solve for the latent heat of fusion.

7. Determine your absolute and percentage error.

8. Repeat for a second trial.

PART B.

1. Fill the calorimeter cup half way with water that is at least 10°C below room temperature. Mass and record the amount of water added to the cup. Cover the calorimeter, insert the thermometer and record the temperature of the system.

2. Insert the rubber tubing from the steam generator (be sure you know the temperature of the steam as it comes from the tube) into the calorimeter and let it bubble into the container until the temperature of the system is at least 10° C higher than room temperature. Remove the steam tube and gently stir until the thermometer no long rises. Record this temperature.

3. Re-mass the calorimeter cup and its contents to find the mass of steam that has condensed and record.

4. Write the heat loss equal heat gain equations and solve for the latent heat of vaporization.

5. Determine your absolute and percentage error.

6. Repeat for a second trial.

Questions

1. If your ice was below 0° C, what correction would you have to make to equation (3) in the theory?

2. If your steam was above 100° C, what correction would you have to make to equation (4) in the theory?

3. Why did you use water below room temperature in Part B?

4. Why did you continue to stir until you reached an equilibrium temperature after you removed the steam tube instead of using the temperature when you pulled the tube from the calorimeter?

5. Why did you dry the ice?

6. Account for your sources of error.

Change of Phase–Heat of Fusion and Heat of Vaporization

Name: _____ Date: _____

Calorimeter material _____ Stirrer material _____

Mass of calorimeter _____ Mass of stirrer _____

Specific heat calorimeter _____ Specific heat stirrer _____

Latent heat of fusion data:

Trial	Mass of water	Initial temperature	Final temperature	Mass of ice	Ice temperature
No.	m	t_i	t_f	m_{ice}	t_o
—	g	°C	°C	g	°C
1					
2					

Latent heat of vaporization data:

Trial	Mass of water	Initial temperature	Final temperature	Mass of steam	Steam temperature
No.	m	t_i	t_f	m_{steam}	t_o
—	g	°C	°C	g	°C
1					
2					

The Velocity of Sound

THEORY

Every kind of sound has its beginning in a vibrating object, the sound source. Surrounding the source is some material (usually a gas) called the medium. The vibrating source produces vibrations in the medium, and these vibrations in the medium are what we call sound waves. We will refer to sound waves as those waves than are in the audible range of frequencies of vibration, namely 20 Hz to 20,000 Hz. Vibrations below 20 Hz are in the subsonic or infrasonic range while those above 20 000 Hz are in the ultrasonic range.

The waves produced by a vibrating object travel outward through the medium with a velocity that is dependent on the medium alone. The velocity of sound in air is 331 m/s at 0° and increases as the temperature of the air increases.

$$v = (331 + .6T)\frac{m}{s} \tag{1}$$

Thus at room temperature, 20°C, the velocity of sound is 343 $\frac{m}{s}$. In denser materials, the speed of transmission increases. In water at 20°C the speed of sound is 1440 $\frac{m}{s}$ and it is about 5000 $\frac{m}{s}$ in steel.

Sound waves represent a particular type of wave motion, called *longitudinal* waves. As the source vibrates, the vibrations are mechanically transferred to the molecules of the medium, and the molecules of the medium vibrate back and forth along the direction of propagation of the wave. Each individual molecule travels only a short distance. The wave itself is the collective motion of a large number of molecules. As the source vibrates, the molecules near the source are first pushed outward, forming a region of pressure higher than the average pressure. The molecules in the high pressure (*compression*) region in turn push against other molecules, and in this fashion a compressive wave travels out from the source. As the vibrating source moves in the other direction, it leaves behind a region of lower pressure (*rarefaction*). Molecules behind the rarefaction rush in to fill this low-pressure region. The rarefaction then seems to move outward from the source in a manner similar to the compression wave. This process is repeated over and over again. A sound wave is thus a series of high pressure (*compression*) and low pressure (*rarefaction*) moving outward from the source through the surrounding medium.

Purpose

To study the phenomenon of resonance and to measure the velocity of sound in air.

Apparatus

Tuning forks, rubber hammer/stopper, water-filled resonance tube, and rubber bands.

Source: Puri
Modified by Zober and Zober

We shall review some of the terminology used to describe wave motion in general. The distance after which the wave pattern begins to repeat itself is called the wavelength, λ. The length can be measured using the distance between successive maxima or successive minima. The time that it takes a complete wave to pass a given point is called the period of vibration, T. If the waves moves with velocity, v, then the wave will have traveled a distance given by

$$\lambda = vT \tag{2}$$

The frequency, f, is the number of complete vibrations in one second. Since period and frequency are reciprocals, equation (2) may be written as

$$v = \lambda f \tag{3}$$

The amplitude of vibration is the difference between the maximum and average pressure or the minimum and average pressure. It is a measure of the energy carried by the wave.

We will consider a case in which a compressive part of a wave from some outside source enters the mouth of a hollow tube of length L that is closed at one end. When the compression wave reaches the closed end of the tube it is reflected and travels back up the tube. Upon reaching the open end of the tube it is reflected again, this time as a rarefaction. The rarefaction now travels down the tube. If the tube is of the proper length, the time spent by the wave traveling up and down the tube is such that the source is producing a rarefaction at the time the first rarefaction is produced by reflection. This rarefaction adds together and travels down the tube as one wave. This process continues until an equilibrium is reached, with the sound growing louder and louder. This phenomenon is known as *resonance* and occurs whenever the length of the tube is

$$\frac{\lambda}{4}, \frac{3}{4}\lambda, \frac{5}{4}\lambda, \frac{7}{4}\lambda, \dots \frac{2n+1}{4}\lambda \tag{4}$$

where n is an integer.

LEARNING OBJECTIVES

After completing this experiment you should be able to do the following:

1. Define compression, rarefaction, and resonance.

2. Be able to relate frequency of a wave and period of vibration.

3. Be able to relate frequency, wavelength, and velocity of a wave.

4. Solve for the velocity of sound using resonance of a column of air.

PROCEDURE

Part of this experiment is to design your own data sheets. Study the procedures to decide how you will do these data sheets.

1. Choose the tuning fork with the lowest frequency. Its frequency has been accurately measured and is stamped on the side of the fork. Strike the prongs of the tuning fork with the rubber hammer or strike the tuning fork with a rubber stopper. Do not strike the lab table with a tuning fork. Hold the vibrating tuning fork over the mouth of the water-filled tube. Lower the water level until the first resonance point is reached, that is, until the sound reaches a maximum intensity. This position can be marked with a rubber band. Measure the distance from the top of the tube to the water level and record your result. (Make two additional determinations for this first resonance point.)

2. Lower the water level slowly and find several other points of resonance. Record these positions. Again make two additional determinations for these points.

3. Repeat on additional tuning forks as required by your instructor.

4. Compute the velocity of sound for each wavelength of a given tuning fork. Find the average velocity and compare it to the velocity of sound in your laboratory on the day of the experiment. What reasons can you give for the possible deviations?

5. Since the air column vibrates a short distance beyond the end of the tube, there is an "end correction". From your data, determine this correction. Is it the same for all frequencies?

QUESTIONS

1. Sound travels at approximately 5000 $\frac{ft}{s}$ in salt water. If the echo from a sonar impulse is heard 10 s after being emitted, how far is the object reflecting the sound from the sonar equipment? (Neglect the temperature correction.)

2. Bats can produce and hear sounds with frequencies up to 100,000 Hz. (a) What is the wavelength of the sound? (b) What is the length of the shortest pipe that would resonate at this frequency?

3. Compute in km, m, cm, and μm, the wavelength from an AM radio station whose assigned frequency is 1020 kHz. The velocity of a radio wave is $3 \times 10^8 \frac{m}{s}$.

Standing Waves

THEORY

Wave motion appears in many physical phenomena, many of which are familiar to us, such as water waves, sound waves, and electromagnetic waves (which include light waves, radio waves, x-rays and more). Waves propagating in a media can be divided into transverse waves and longitudinal waves. A wave travelling through a string is an example of a transverse wave since the particles of the string are moving along a vertical axis (the vibrator in our experiment moves the string up and down) whereas the wave disturbance we observe moves along the horizontal axis and therefore transverse (or perpendicular) to the actual motion of the particles. The molecular forces that bind the particles together transmit the up and down motion from one end of the string to the other and thus the wave "travels" or "propagates." (See Figure 19.1).

Purpose

(a) We will study a transverse wave propagating through a linear medium (a string), observing the standing wave pattern produced in that media. (b) We will determine the linear mass density of the string.

Apparatus

Vibrator with two strings (one light, and one heavy), slotted masses, additional slotted mass of 1g, 2g, and 5g, mass hanger, meterstick, and strobe light if available.

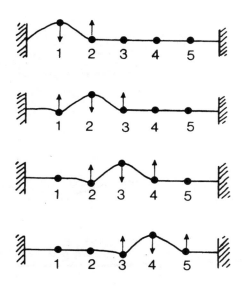

Figure 19.1

An interesting phenomena occurs in transverse waves when one end of the string is fixed and not allowed to oscillate. When the wave reaches the fixed (or stationary) point, it will be reflected back across the string. If the loss in amplitude upon reflection is negligible, the incident and reflected waves will form a system of two identical waves travelling in opposite directions through the same medium and the position of a particle on the string, at any time, will be a sum of the displacements of the two waves at that position. The "pattern" produced depends on the relative phase of the two waves. If the length of the string coincides with 1/2, 2/2 . . . n/2 of a wavelength of the wave, then the wave will be in its zero amplitude position when it reaches the fixed point and will be reflected back "in phase" with the incident wave resulting in a standing wave pattern [Figure 19.2(a)]. If the length of the string does not permit n/2 wavelengths, then the reflected wave will be out of phase with the incident wave and destructive interference will be observed resulting in no pattern [Figure 19.2(b)]. Therefore, the condition for a standing wave is:

$$L = \frac{n}{2}\lambda \qquad (1)$$

where n is the number of antinodes in the pattern and λ is the wavelength. An antinode is a point of maximum amplitude in the standing wave pattern. The points on the pattern that remain motionless are called the nodes. In our experiment, the segment of the string in contact with the pulley may be regarded as a node.

The velocity, v, of a transverse wave on a string is given by:

$$v = \sqrt{\frac{F}{M_L}} \qquad (2)$$

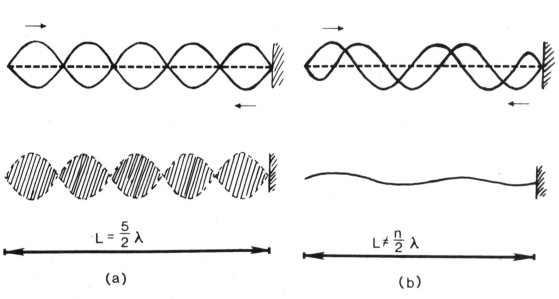

$$L = \frac{5}{2}\lambda \qquad\qquad L \neq \frac{n}{2}\lambda$$

(a)   (b)

Figure 19.2

where F is the tension of the string and m_L is the linear mass density (mass per unit length) of the string. In our experiment, the tension of the string will be provided by the weight of hooked mass at the end of the string (see Figure 19.3). Therefore,

$$v = \sqrt{\frac{Mg}{m_L}} \qquad (3)$$

For any type of wave, the relationship between the velocity, v, of the wave, its frequency, f, and its wavelength, λ, is given by

$$v = f\lambda. \qquad (4)$$

Combining Equations (1), (3) and (4), we obtain an expression for the linear mass density of the string:

$$M_L = \frac{M(n')^2 g}{4f^2 (L')^2} \qquad (5)$$

We shall set up several standing wave patterns and measure the elements of Equation 5. After solving for m_L, we will compare our results to the true m_L of the string to test the validity of this equation.

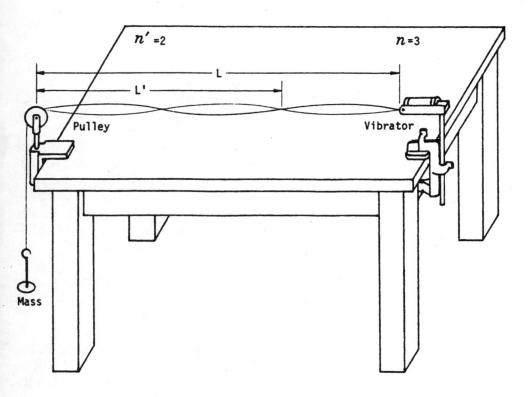

Figure 19.3

After completing the experiment, you should be able to do the following.

1. Define what is meant by a transverse waveform and give an example.

2. Draw a transverse waveform, indicating the wavelength of the wave between successive maxima or successive minima, show the amplitude of the wave and make some notation about the frequency of the wave.

3. Differentiate between nodes and antinodes.

4. Explain why the fixed ends of a vibrating string are nodal points.

5. Show the unit conversion for equation (2) is dimensionally correct.

PROCEDURE

(All data should be recorded on the data sheet provided.)

1. Take one of the strings, pass it over the groove in the pulley and hang a weight on the string to temporarily hold it in place. Plug in the vibrator. Now add enough mass at the end of the string so that you are observing three antinodes (For the thin black string, start with 250 gms and for the thick black string start with 450 gms.) Continue adjusting M until you obtain the maximum amplitude for the antinodes. Observe that the node near the vibrator is distorted. To correct for this, you will *always neglect the antinode near the vibrator and only consider the remaining $n' = n-1$ antinodes.* Record M, n', and L' (the length of n' node-antinode-node patterns). Measure this length to one decimal place in cms. (See Figure 19.3.)

2. To obtain the uncertainty in the length, $\Delta L'$, observe that the nodes are not clearly defined points but are "spread out." Measure the length of this spreading or smearing of the node to one decimal place in cms.

3. To obtain the uncertainty in the mass, ΔM, add additional mass to M until the maximum amplitude of the antinode is reduced to one-half of its value (you can roughly measure this if you place a meterstick behind the wave pattern). The additional mass you have added is ΔM.

4. Now, for the same string, form a pattern of 4($n' = 3$) or 2($n' = 1$) antinodes and measure M, n', L', $\Delta L'$, and ΔM.

5. Repeat 1 through 4 for the other string.

6. If time permits, observe the vibrating string with a stroboscope. Observe that you can "stop" the motion by tuning the frequency of the stroboscope to multiples of 120 cps, which is the frequency of the vibrator.

QUESTIONS

1. For your first pattern, determine m_L and Δm_L with your data. Show your work below and use the correct number of significant figures.

$$m_L = \frac{M\,(n')^2 g}{4f^2\,(L')^2} \qquad \Delta m_L = m_L\sqrt{\left(\tfrac{\Delta M}{M}\right)^2 + 2\left(\frac{\Delta L'}{L'}\right)^2}$$

List m_L and Δm_L for your other patterns below.

2. Obtain the correct mass values for the thick black string and the thin black string from your instructor. Compare each of your experimental values of m_L to the correct value. In each case, did the correct value fall within the range of your experimental values? Explain.

Standing Waves

Name: _____   Lab Section #: _____

Date: _____   Lab Partners: _____

I. DATA

Thin Black String

n	n´	L´ (cm)	ΔL´ (cm)	M (g)	ΔM (g)

Thick Black String

n	n´	L´ (cm)	ΔL´ (cm)	M (g)	ΔM (g)

The Electric Field

THEORY

For reasons we do not fully understand, an electrical charge produces an electrical field. The electrical field, or E-field, is a modification of space. When another charge is placed into the E-field it experiences electrical force. If both charges are of the same charge the force will be one of electrostatic repulsion where if they have opposite charge they will attract with an electrostatic force that is described by Coulomb's law. In his work on electromagnetism, Michael Faraday (1791 to 1867), introduced an ingenious way of visualizing electric fields with his imaginary *electric field lines*. These imaginary lines are drawn in such a manner that their direction at any point is the same direction of the electric field at that point.

As we will discover in this experiment there are five rules that are followed when the computer draws field lines:

1. The direction of the field line at any point in the field is the same as the direction that a positive charge would move if placed at that point.

2. The spacing of field lines is such that they are close where the field is strong and far apart where the field is weak.

3. Positive charges are a source of field lines where negative charges are a sink for field lines. Field lines behave as if they leave a positive charge and enter a negative one.

4. Electric field lines are always perpendicular to the source or sink.

5. Electric field lines never cross.

Purpose

To explore, using computer simulated static charges, electrical field lines and electrical field intensity vectors that surround combinations of charges.

Apparatus

Macintosh or PC computer, EM Field® Program from Physics Academic Software, drawing materials (paper and colored pencils or pens).

After completing this experiment you should be able to do the following:

1. Understand that positive charges are an electrical field source and that negative charges are electrical field sinks.

2. Electric lines are only a visualization of the field; they do not exist but are used to indicate the direction and relative strength of the field.

3. Electric lines never intersect.

4. Equipotential lines never intersect.

5. Field lines are always perpendicular to equipotential lines.

PROCEDURE

1. Note that across the top bar on the screen, from left to right, there are five items relating to the computer program. These are:

Options   **File**   **Sources**   **Field & Potential**   **Display**

Using the mouse, place the pointer on the menu bar item **Sources,** click and drag down to 3D point charges and release. This will open a screen called *3D Electric Field Vector*s.

2. Place the pointer on the bar item **Display,** click and drag down the screen to *Show Grid*. Now release the mouse. There should now be a grid across the screen.

3. Place the pointer of the mouse at the bottom of the screen on a solid red charge of 1, click, hold, and drag the charge to the center of the screen. Release the mouse. The solid red (positive) charge should be at the center of the computer screen.

The solid charges represent positive charges and the open ones, negative charge.

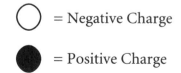

4. Our only concern in this laboratory exploration will be the first three contents under the **Field & Potential** menu on the item bar. Click on it and drag the menu down. Observe that the contents are:

Field vectors
Directional arrows
Field lines
Potential
Potential Difference
Equipotentials
Equipotentials with numbers

5. Drag down to *Field lines* and release. Place the pointer on the screen near the surface of your charge and release. It traces out a field line, a Faraday electric field line. Make 12 or more of the field lines around the charge. You may need to practice this a few times. To erase the field lines around your charge, place the pointer on the bar item **Display** and drag down to *Clean Up Screen*. Check with your instructor to see if your generated electrical field patterns can be downloaded and printed. If not use paper and colored pencils or pens and sketch your computer generated E-field as neatly as is possible.

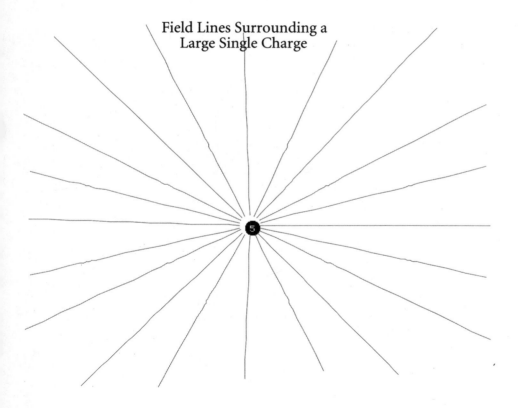

Field Lines Surrounding a
Large Single Charge

6. Using the mouse, again place the pointer on the bar item **Sources,** click and drag down to 3D point charges and release. This will give you a screen called *3D Electric Field Vectors*. Place the pointer of the mouse at the bottom of the screen on a solid red charge, click, hold, and drag the charge to right of center of the screen. Release the mouse. Once again place the pointer of the mouse at the bottom of the screen but this time on an open charge (negative), click, hold, and drag the charge to left of center of the screen along the same straight line as in the diagram below. Release the mouse.

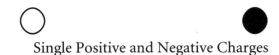

Single Positive and Negative Charges

Click on **Field & Potential** menu on the item bar; drag down to *Field lines* and release. Place the pointer on the screen near a surface of one of your charges and release. It traces out a field line. Make 12 or more of the field lines around the charge. You may practice a few times. To erase the field lines around your charge, place the pointer on the

bar item **Display** and drag down to *Clean up screen*. If your instructor has approved downloading your generated electrical field pattern then do so. If not use paper and the colored pencils or pens and sketch the E-field pattern as neatly as is possible.

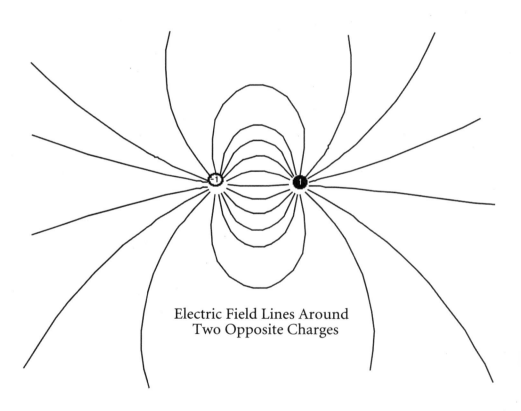

Electric Field Lines Around
Two Opposite Charges

7. Repeat procedure 6 for two equal negative charges.

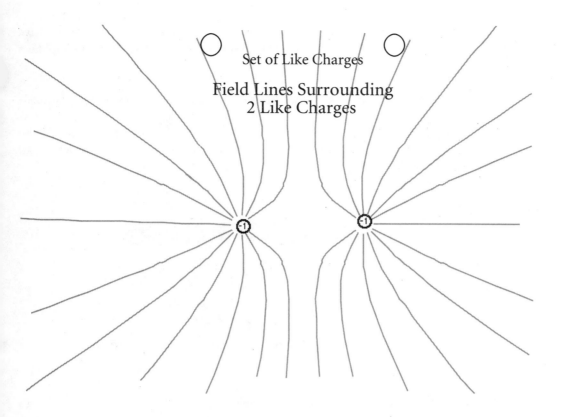

Set of Like Charges

Field Lines Surrounding
2 Like Charges

8. Repeat procedure 7 for two unequal opposite charges.

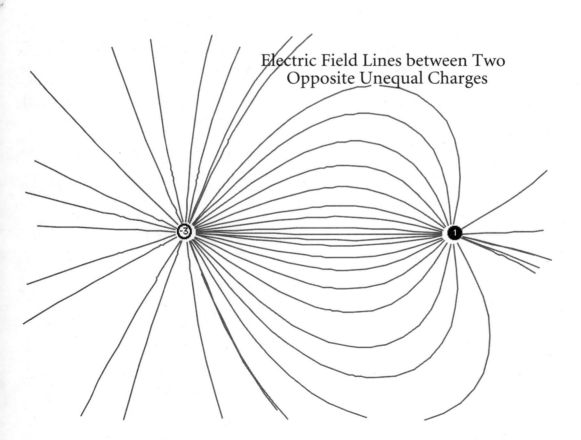

Electric Field Lines between Two
Opposite Unequal Charges

9. Repeat procedure 6 for three unequal positive charges and a negative charge all arranged in a square. Download and print your field or make a drawing.

10. Repeating the basic procedures of procedure 6, arrange ten equal positive charges and ten negative charges as shown below. The arrangement simulates a parallel plate capacitor. Investigate the field between and around the simulated capacitor. Be sure to make a sketch of the situation or download and print.

Parallel Plate Capacitor Arrangement

11. Repeat procedures 3 and 4, dragging down to *Directional arrows* and release. Map out and sketch the field using this command for a single positive charge. The directional arrows simply point to the direction of the field at a particular point in space surrounding a charge.

12. Repeat procedure 11 for two unlike but equal charges.

13. Repeat procedures 3, 4, and 11, this time dragging down to *Field vectors* and release. Map out and sketch the field using this command for a single positive charge. The field vectors will vary in length corresponding to the position in the field and the field intensity at that point. The field vectors will also point from a positive charge toward a negative charge.

14. Repeat procedure 11 for two unlike but equal charges.

15. Explore drawing equipotential lines around several charge arrangements as in procedures 5, 6, 7, and 8.

QUESTIONS

1. Can an electric field line begin and end on the same conductor?

2. Why is the surface of a conductor considered to be an equipotential surface?

3. Two charges of $+10.0 \ \mu C$ are 5 cm apart in vacuum. What is the magnitude of the field at the midpoint between the two charges?

4. Repeat question 3 for charges of $+10.0\ \mu C$ and $-10.0\ \mu C$.

5. What is the electrostatic force acting on the $-10\ \mu C$ charge in problem 4?

6. Given an E-field of $5.0 \times 10^5\ \dfrac{N}{C}$ at a point in space. A charge of $+2.0$ nC is placed at that point, what force does the charge experience? The $+2.0$ nC particle has a mass of 4.0 mg. If this particle is released from rest, what initial acceleration will it experience?

Electricity

THEORY

Perhaps you have walked across a carpet in the wintertime, touched a door-knob or some other metallic object, and experienced the resulting nerve-jolting shock. Or maybe on a dry day you have noticed pieces of lint clinging to your clothing. These two phenomena are related and ancient man observed similar effects, although the early Greeks are usually credited with the discovery. Early experimenters found that substances such as rubber, hard wax, and amber acquired the capability to exert forces on other objects whenever they had been rubbed vigorously with pieces of wool or fur. These substances were said to be *electrified* or possess the *eletrick vertue*. It was thought that the *electrick vertue* was a remarkable fluid that flowed from one body to another. Today we say that a given object is charged, and instead of talking about *vertue* we use the term *electric charge*.

The American statesman and natural philosopher, Benjamin Franklin, investigated electrical phenomena and advanced the theory that electrical effects were due to surplus or deficit of a single fluid. He assigned the terms *positive* to represent a surplus and *negative* to represent a deficit of this fluid. Franklin believed that when a hard rubber rod was rubbed with fur, electrical fluid flowed from the rod to the fur. Thus the charge on the rod was negative. The basic discoveries made by Franklin and others were extended and quantified by a host of scientists until today electricity is a well-understood subject with far-ranging technical applications. Whenever we turn on an electric light, use the telephone, or watch television, we are utilizing the end results of a lengthy chain of scientific discoveries and investigations that started usually as a result of some man's curiosity. Intellectual curiosity, as much as anything else, has transformed our world.

Electric charge is no longer viewed as being a fluid; rather, we have an atomistic and a wave notion of electricity. Numerous experiments have shown that there is a smallest amount of negative charge, namely the charge on the electron. The corresponding amount of positive charge is the charge found on the proton. Every electron in nature has the same charge as every other electron. We say that the electron's charge is quantized. So is the proton's charge. Every proton in nature has the same charge as all others. Both the electron and proton have the same magnitude of charge. We assign the symbol e to this elementary charge. The elementary charge is quite small, so we assign a larger unit, the coulomb, C, which is the charge of a definite number of electrons (6.24×10^{18} e or 6.24 billion billion electrons have a charge of 1 coulomb). The elementary charge is: e = 1.6022×10^{-19} C.

Purpose

To study some methods of understanding electrical charges and their behavior.

Apparatus

Three 6.3 V lamps, 3 sockets, connecting wires, 2 No. 6 dry cells, and a momentary switch.

Source: Puri
Modified by Zober and Zober

It is found that some materials can hold a stationary charge. That is, if some charge is placed on a portion of an object made of that material, the charge will remain in that locality. Such materials are called insulators. Other materials allow charge to move about freely and these are called conductors. Glass, rubber, and plastic are examples of insulators, while copper, silver, and salt water are conductors. Not all materials fit neatly into these two categories. Some materials, known as semiconductors, are intermediate between conductors and insulators. Our modern technology utilizes these materials extensively, the transistor radio is a notable example.

Our major interest in electricity lies in the fact that it makes possible the efficient transmission of energy over long distances. Thermal energy from fossil fuels or nuclear reactors is converted into electrical energy that is carried by conduction wires to our homes and schools. This electrical energy can be used for light and heat or to operate a computer.

The movement of electrical charge is responsible for the transmission of electrical energy. A moving charge is called a *current*. The unit of current is the ampere, A, named in honor of the French physicist Andrè Marie Ampéré (1775 to 1836). A current of one ampere consists of one coulomb of charge moving through a wire of a given cross-sectional area in one second of time.

Since electric current carries energy, we can extract this energy and change it into heat and work. As an example, let us consider the case of the incandescent electric light. Electric charge flows into a connection called a terminal, moves through the filament (a poor conductor with a high melting point), and exits by the other terminal. Clearly some of the energy possessed by the charge that enters the light has been transformed into light and heat. There is a difference in charge energy between the terminals. This energy difference per unit charge is measured by the *potential difference* across the terminals. This potential difference is given a special unit of measurement called the *volt*, V, after the Italian scientist, Count Alessandro Volta (1745 to 1827).

Components of an electrical circuit that suffer a potential difference across their terminals are called *resistors*. Resistors impede current and "use up" voltage, the potential difference. Resistors convert electrical energy into heat. The filament of an incandescent electric light has a high resistance and converts the electrical energy into radiant energy, heat and light. Resistors have a *resistance*, R.

The maintenance of an electric current in a system that uses energy requires some nonelectrical energy source, or *emf*, E. Normally this is supplied by a mechanical driven generator, but occasionally we use batteries that change chemical energy into electrical energy. A measure of emf is the amount of work done per unit charge by the nonelectrical energy source. The unit of emf is the volt, but you should be careful not to confuse emf with the totally different concept of potential difference.

When we discuss electrical appliances, we are not usually interested in the total energy consumed but the rate of energy consumption. This is easy to calculate from the basic definitions. We define V as the potential difference across a set of terminals and the current through the conductor as the current, I. Potential difference is the work done per unit charge or $V = \dfrac{W}{q}$ where q is the charge through the conductor. Current is charge per unit time or $I = \dfrac{q}{t}$. Multiplying these terms:

$$V \times I = \frac{W}{q} \times \frac{q}{t} = \frac{W}{t}$$

And we define power as

$$P = \frac{W}{t}$$

The *power*, P, consumed by the conductor is expressed in watts, W, and is the product of the current and the potential difference, or:

$$P = IV$$

In order to produce a steady electrical current, we must provide an unbroken conducting path that begins and ends at an energy source such as a battery or a generator. In this experiment we will use batteries. This complete conducting path is called an *electrical circuit*. Batteries and generators do not create charge; they merely move existing charge around the electrical circuit, much the same as a pump moves water in a pipe. Just as we can control the flow of water by means of a valve, so we can control the flow of electrical current by means of a switch, which is simply a convenient device for making a break in the circuit.

In order to describe an electrical circuit to someone else, or to remember for your own use, it is helpful to draw a diagram of the circuit. The method we use is to draw a diagram of each of the components in the circuit and then draw lines showing how the wires were connected. This circuit diagram is called a *schematic diagram*. Each of the components in an electrical circuit has been given a special symbol. These special symbols allow us to draw a schematic diagram. Several of the basic schematic diagram symbols for the components used in circuit diagrams are shown in Figure 21.1. A line represents a wire. The battery is represented by a set of unequal parallel lines where the longer line symbolizes the positive terminal and the shorter the negative terminal and is marked with an E for the emf. Resistors such as light bulbs are shown with a saw-tooth line and are marked with an R. An open switch, S, is shown as a break in the circuit.

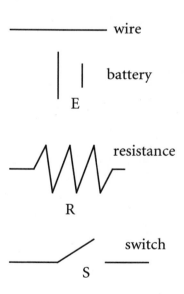

Figure 21.1

After completing this experiment you should be able to do the following:

1. Define:
   potential difference
   resistance
   emf
   current
   power

2. Know the units for current, potential difference, resistance, emf, and power.

3. Be able to connect the components of a circuit from a schematic diagram.

4. Draw the correct schematic for a given circuit.

PROCEDURE

You are to design your own data sheets in this experiment. Your data will be a series of schematic diagrams of the circuits that you will wire in the following procedures. Be as neat and complete as possible when making the schematics. You are to answer the questions that relate each part of the experiment in your data.

PART A. SIMPLE CIRCUIT

1. Connect a wire from the positive terminal of a battery to one end of the switch, a wire from the other end of the switch to one terminal of the light socket, and a wire from the other terminal of the socket to the negative terminal of the battery. In each case be sure that the metal part of the connecting wire is connected rather than the outer covering.

2. The schematic diagram for this circuit has been drawn below. For the remainder of this experiment you will have to draw your own schematics.

3. Close the switch. Does the bulb light?

4. What is the purpose of the outer covering on the wire?

schematic for a simple circuit

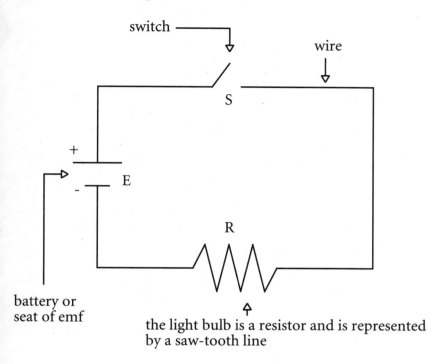

the light bulb is a resistor and is represented
by a saw-tooth line

Figure 21.2

PART B. BATTERIES IN SERIES

1. Remove the wire connected to the positive terminal of the first battery.
Connect it to the positive terminal of the second battery. Connect another
wire from the positive terminal of the first battery to the negative terminal
of the second battery. The batteries are now connected in *series.*

2. Draw a schematic of this circuit.

3. After gaining approval from your instructor, close the switch. How does
the brightness of the bulb compare with that of Part A?

4. What conclusion can you draw from this comparison?

PART C. BATTERIES IN PARALLEL

1. Return to the circuit of Part A. Connect a wire from the positive terminal
of the first battery to the positive terminal of the second battery. Next, connect another wire from the negative terminal of the first battery to the negative terminal of the second. The batteries are now connected in *parallel.*

2. Draw a schematic of this circuit.

3. After gaining approval from your instructor, close the switch. How does the brightness of the bulb compare with that of Part A?

4. What conclusion can you draw from this comparison?

PART D. BULBS IN SERIES

1. Construct the circuit of Part B and add a second bulb in series with the first.

2. Draw a schematic of this circuit.

3. After gaining approval from your instructor, close the switch. How does the brightness of the bulb compare with that of Part A or Part B?

4. Unscrew one of the bulbs. What happens?

5. What conclusion can you draw from this comparison?

6. Add a third bulb in series and repeat the above procedures for Part D.

PART E. BULBS IN PARALLEL

1. Using the circuit of Part B, add a second bulb in parallel with the first.

2. Draw a schematic of this circuit.

3. After gaining approval from your instructor, close the switch. Is the brightness of each bulb closer to that of Part A or Part B?

4. Unscrew one of the bulbs. What happens?

5. What conclusion can you draw from this comparison?

6. Add a third bulb in parallel and repeat the above procedures for Part E. Unscrew two bulbs. What happens?

QUESTIONS

1. A bulb burns out in a series circuit. What happens to the other bulbs?

2. A bulb burns out in a parallel circuit. What happens to the other bulbs? Why?

3. A current of 2.7 A exists in a lamp for 5 minutes. How much charge passes through the lamp in this time period?

4. If 1400 C flows through a lamp bulb in 1 minute, what is the current?

Resistors and Ohm's Law

THEORY

Ohm's Law states that for most conducting materials, called ohmic materials, the voltage drop across the conductor is directly proportional to the current in the conductor and the resistance of the conductor.

$$V = IR \qquad (1)$$

Where I is the current in amperes, A, R is the resistance in ohms, Ω, and V is the voltage drop in volts, V.

The experimental setup for measuring the resistance of a resistor is shown in the figure below.

The rheostat is a variable resistor, R_{vab}, used to regulate the current from the power supply, to control the voltage across a resistor, and to protect the meters used in the circuit. Ammeters are used to measure the current at a certain point in a circuit. They are always connected in series in a circuit. Voltmeters measure the drop in voltage across a given resistance. Voltmeters are always connected in parallel with the resistor under study.

Resistance spools are lengths of wire of a specific gauge wound to a size that has a specific resistance. *Gauge number* is related to the diameter of the wire. See the tables in the Appendix for gauge numbers and wire diameters. The *resistivity*, ρ, of a conductor is a function of the metal of which the wire is made.

Purpose

To investigate the properties of resistors and to verify Ohm's Law.

Apparatus

DC ammeter (0 to 3.0 A), DC voltmeter (0 to 7.5 V), rheostat (10 to 20 ohms), 2 No. 6 dry cells, momentary contact switch, connecting wire, junction clips, and 3 resistance spools: 30 gauge 200 cm nickel-silver, 28 gauge 200 cm nickel silver, and 2000 cm 30 gauge copper. Constantan or German-silver spools may be used.

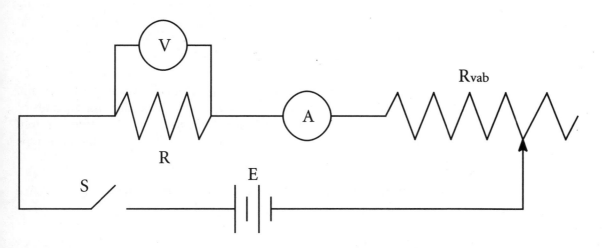

Figure 22,1

Source: Puri
Modified by Zober and Zober

The resistivity of a given wire is expressed as

$$\rho = \frac{RA}{L} \qquad (2)$$

Where L is the length of the wire wrapping in the resistance spool, A is the cross-sectional area of the wire, and R is the resistance. The gauge number will give the diameter, d, and the area is found from

$$A = \frac{\pi d^2}{4} \qquad (3)$$

LEARNING OBJECTIVES

After completing this experiment you should be able to do the following:

1. To read a schematic diagram of a circuit and use it to correctly connect the components of the diagram.

2. Calculate the resistance of a resistor from Ohm's law.

3. Show that equation (2) is dimensionally correct.

4. Calculate the resistance of a resistor from equation (2).

5. Know the 4 factors that determine the resistance of a resistor.

PROCEDURE

1. With the exception of hooking up the batteries, connect the apparatus according to the schematic of Figure 22.1 making sure that the meters are connected with the correct polarity. Use one of the resistance spools, R, as the unknown resistance. Do not connect the batteries until you have approval from your instructor.

2. Close the switch and adjust the rheostat to give a current reading of 0.1 A then read and record the voltage drop across the voltmeter. Open the switch as soon as the reading is made. Repeat this procedure for currents of 0.2 A, 0.4 A, 0.6 A, 0.8 A, and 1.0 A. Use these points to plot a V vs. I graph. Use the graph to determine the slope of the curve. What does the slope represent?

3. Repeat procedure 2 for a second resistance spool. What is the difference in these two graphs? What is the resistance of the second spool?

4. Repeat procedure 3 for a third resistance spool. What are the differences between these graphs? What is the resistance of the third resistance spool?

5. Use the information in the Resistivity Table and Wire Gauge Table in the Appendix to calculate the accepted value of the resistance of each spool. Compare the resistance of spool 1 to the slope of the line of the graph for spool 1. Repeat for the two remaining spools. Comment on your sources of error.

QUESTIONS

1. What happens to the voltage in a resistor when the resistance is doubled and the current is constant?

2. If you were asked to design a heating element for a new toaster, would you choose a copper wire or tungsten to make the heating element? Why?

3. What happens to a resistor if you double the length? What happens if you double the diameter of the wire?

4. Does a resistor have a positive or a negative end? If it is placed in a circuit what determines the polarity of the ends?

Resistors and Ohm's Law

Name: _____   Date: _____

Spool 1   Material _____   Length _____   Gauge number _____

Trial No.	Current I A	Voltage V V
1	0.1	
2	0.2	
3	0.4	
4	0.6	
5	0.8	
6	1.0	

Spool 2   Material _____   Length _____   Gauge number _____

Trial No.	Current I A	Voltage V V
1	0.1	
2	0.2	
3	0.4	
4	0.6	
5	0.8	
6	1.0	

Spool 3   Material _____   Length _____   Gauge number _____

Trial No.	Current I A	Voltage V V
1	0.1	
2	0.2	
3	0.4	
4	0.6	
5	0.8	
6	1.0	

Internal Resistance of a Cell

THEORY

Ohm's Law for a complete electrical circuit is written as

$$E = I \sum R \qquad (1)$$

Where I is the current maintained by the battery or DC power source, E is the emf of the source, and $\sum R$ is the resistance of the entire circuit. $\sum R$ is the total resistance of the external circuit and the *internal resistance*, r, of the cell. The internal resistance of a cell is dependent on the type of cell and its age. Storage cells like the lead-sulfuric type usually have a very small internal resistance. Dry cells usually have much higher internal resistance and it increases as the cell becomes older. Continued use of a dry cell causes a build up of tiny hydrogen gas bubbles around the anode increasing the internal resistance. Warming a battery will cause some of the hydrogen to dissolve into the surrounding manganese dioxide paste reducing the internal resistance. This is a temporary fix because the hydrogen bubbles will reform.

Purpose

To study the relationship between internal resistance and the current through a cell.

Apparatus

One "older" No. 6 dry cell, one new No. 6 dry cell rheostat (25 ohm range), dual range DC ammeter 0 to 1 A/0 to 10 A, DC voltmeter 0 to 7.5 V range, connecting write, junction clips, and a momentary switch.

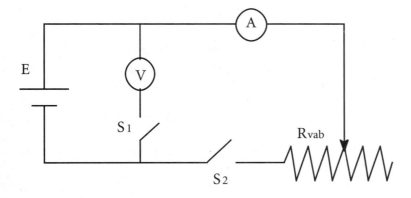

Figure 23.1

Consider the diagram shown above. With switch S_1 closed and S_2 open the voltmeter will read the potential difference across the cell. Since the voltmeter has a very high resistance and draws negligible current, this potential difference is practically the emf, E, of the cell. When switch S_2 is closed, the current I flows through the external circuit and Ohm's Law can be written as

$$I = \frac{E}{R + r} \qquad (2)$$

Source: Puri
Modified by Zober and Zober

As long as switch S_2 is closed the voltmeter will read the terminal voltage, V_t, an amount less than E. After eliminating R, the internal resistance of the cell is then

$$r = \frac{E - V_t}{I} \qquad (3)$$

LEARNING OBJECTIVES

After completing this experiment you should be able to do the following:

1. Define and relate emf and terminal potential difference.

2. Show that equation (3) is dimensionally correct.

3. How does the internal resistance of a dry cell battery change as it ages? Is this also true for alkaline batteries?

PROCEDURE

1. Connect the apparatus as in Figure 23.1 using an *old* No. 6 dry cell. Close switch S_1 and read the voltmeter and record the emf, E, of the battery. Now close switch S_2 and read the voltmeter and the ammeter. Record your readings.

2. Change the setting of the rheostat and obtain another set of readings. Run 6 trials spacing them about equally from minimum to maximum currents.

3. Replace the "old" cell with a new one and follow the above procedures.

4. While taking the readings of V and I, keep a close watch on the product IV. Observe the maximum value and after the maximum is reached, the product IV drops off. Plot a graph of the product IV vs. I and another graph of the product EI vs. I. The product IV is the useful power and the product EI gives the total power.

QUESTIONS

1. Plot a graph for each cell on the same sheet of graph paper showing internal resistance as a function of the current drawn from the cell. What does the curve show regarding the variation of the internal resistance with the current drawn from the cell?

2. Plot another set of graphs showing terminal voltage as a function of the current drawn from the cell. What does the curve show regarding the variation of the terminal voltage of a cell with the current drawn from it?

3. The voltmeter draws a tiny current. Does this affect your data?

4. If the external resistance of a circuit is 20 Ω, the emf of the cell is 100 V, and the current is 4 A, what is the internal resistance of the cell?

Internal Resistance of a Cell

Name: _____   Date: _____

Old Cell

Trial No.	emf E V	Voltage V V	Current I A
1			
2			
3			
4			
5			
6			

New Cell

Trial	emf E	Voltage V	Current I
No.	V	V	A
1			
2			
3			
4			
5			
6			

Resistivity/Resistance

THEORY

The resistance, R, of a section of circular wire depends upon several factors: (a) the resistivity, ρ, of the material, (b) its diameter, d, or radius, r, and (c) its length, L, according to the relationship

$$R = \rho \frac{L}{A} \qquad (1)$$

The cross sectional area, A, can be calculated by

$$A = \pi r^2 = \frac{1}{4} \pi d^2$$

Substituting this into equation (1) yields

$$R = \rho \frac{L}{\frac{1}{4}\pi d^2} = \frac{4\rho L}{\pi d^2}$$

Clearing fractions

$$\pi R d^2 = 4\rho L$$

Then solving for the resistivity gives

$$\rho = \frac{\pi R d^2}{4L} \qquad (2)$$

In this experiment we will use coils of circular wire as resistors. One of the resistors is copper. The particular copper alloy we will be using has a resistivity of $1.78 \times 10^{-8}\ \Omega\text{m}$. A second material we may use in this experiment is a copper alloy known as *constatan*. Constatan is 60% Cu and 40% Ni and has a resistivity of $54.57 \times 10^{-8}\ \Omega\text{m}$. The third material is nickel-silver, but it does not contain silver. It is an alloy of copper that is 65% Cu, 18% Ni, and 17% Zn. Nickel silver has a resistivity of $58.60 \times 10^{-8}\ \Omega\text{m}$.

When a current, I, is put through a resistor, R, there is a drop in voltage across the resistor according to Ohm's Law, V = IR. If the current through the resistor is measured by an ammeter and the voltage drop by a voltmeter, we can calculate the resistance by:

Purpose

To theoretically calculate the resistance of a series of wire resistors and to verify the values experimentally.

Apparatus

DC ammeter (0 to 3.0 A), DC voltmeter (0 to 7.5 V), 3 No. 6 dry cells, momentary contact switch, connecting wire, junction clips, and 3 resistance spools: 30 gauge 200 cm nickel-silver, 28 gauge 200 cm nickel-silver, and a 2000 cm 30 gauge copper resistance spool. Constantan or German-silver spools may be substituted. There will be 2 spools of unknown materials with length and gauge number.

$$R = \frac{V}{I} \qquad \text{(3)}$$

In this experiment we will determine experimental values for 3 spools of known resistivity and compare the results with accepted values. Then we will determine the resistivity of 2 unknowns and will attempt to identify them.

PROCEDURE

Part of this experiment is to design your own data sheets. Study the procedures to decide how you will do these data sheets.

PART A. CALCULATED RESISTANCE

1. Locate the 3 small spools of wire you will use in part of the experiment. One of them is copper and the other two are nickel-silver. Note the length and gauge number of the wire wrapped about the spool. The values are in cgs units. You will have to convert the length into the SI. You will find the diameter of the wire in the Wire Gauge Table in the Appendix.

2. Record the SI values in your data.

3. Using equation (1), the length, diameter, and the accepted resistivity calculate the resistance of each spool.

4. Record your values in your data.

PART B. EXPERIMENTAL RESISTANCE

5. Connect your voltmeter, ammeter, batteries, contact switch, and the copper resistance spool as shown in Figure 24.1. Do not connect to the batteries until you have approval from your instructor. Be sure to seek your instructor's approval before continuing.

6. After approval, close the contact switch and as carefully and accurately as you can read the current, I, in the circuit and the voltage drop, V, across the resistor. Release the contact switch.

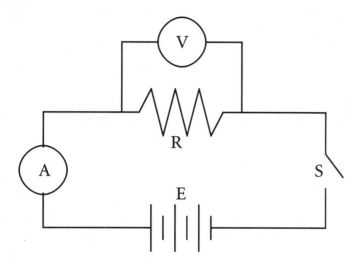

Figure 24.1

7. Make a total of 3 trials measuring and recording the current and voltage drop in each case.

8. Average the currents and voltage drops and use equation (3) to determine the experimental resistance of the resistor.

9. Calculate the average resistance of the spool.

10. Compare your experimental value to the value in Part 1. Find the experimental error and the percent error.

11. Remove the copper spool from your circuit and substitute the 28 gauge nickel-silver spool and repeat procedures of Part B.

12. Repeat procedures of Part B this time using the 30 gauge nickel-silver resistance spool.

PART C. RESISTIVITIES OF UNKNOWN SPOOLS

13. Remove the nickel-silver spool and replace it with one of the unknown spools.

14. Make a series of 3 trials measuring and recording the current and voltage drop. Record your data.

15. Use the average current and voltage drop and calculate the experimental resistance of this spool.

16. Find the diameter of the spool from the gauge number. Using equation (2), the length of the wire, its diameter, and the experimental resistance, calculate the resistivity of the spool.

17. Replace this spool with the second unknown. Repeat the procedures of Part C.

18. Identify the material of the two unknown resistance spools. What are they? What error and percent error is involved?

QUESTIONS

1. Did the ammeter and voltmeter you connected in the circuit effect the outcome of the experiment?

2. How does the resistance of the coil change as the temperature increases?

3. Investigate a resistance thermometer. What major advantage does it have over a liquid thermometer?

4. A 6 V source is applied to the ends of a 30 gauge copper coil that has a length of 200 m. What current exists within the coil?

5. We did not investigate temperature variance in this experiment. Knowing the temperature coefficient of resistance, α, of a material we can solve for changes in resistance using

$$\alpha = \frac{\Delta R}{R_o \Delta T}$$

R_o is the room temperature resistance. Given a copper resistor with a room temperature resistance of 4.39 Ω, what is the change in the resistance if the temperature changes by 80° C? The temperature coefficient of resistance is $0.004 \frac{1}{C°}$.

Resistors in Series and Parallel

THEORY

A series circuit consists of devices connected in a single closed path. The current provided by the power supply can only travel in this closed path, thus

$$I_t = I_1 = I_2 = I_3$$

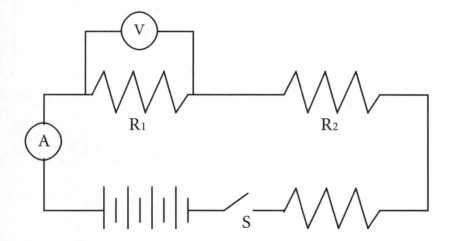

Figure 25.1

Knowing that Ohm's Law, $V = IR$, applies to any part of the circuit as well as the entire circuit, the energy transferred per unit charge, $V = \dfrac{W}{q}$, to each device in the series circuit must equal the total supplied to the circuit.

$$V = IR \text{ thus } V_1 = I_1 R_1, \ V_2 = I_2 R_2, \ V_3 = I_3 R_3$$

And

$$V_t = V_1 + V_2 + V_3$$

Since the current must be the same,

$$R_t = R_1 + R_2 + R_3$$

Source: Zober and Zober

Purpose

To show that (a) current is the same and voltage is additive in a series circuit (b) that voltage is the same and current is additive for a parallel circuit. Then (c) apply these relationships to series-parallel networks.

Apparatus

Various 0.5-watt resistors, 10 Ω to 100 Ω range, SPST switch, ammeter (0 to 5A), milliammeter, voltmeter (0 to 7.5 V), millivoltmeter, a variable power supply or 4 No. 6 V dry cells, junction connectors, and connecting wires. A breadboard is helpful, but not necessary for this lab.

In parallel, two or more conducting paths are connected to common points in the circuit. These paths divide the current; charge entering a common point must equal the current leaving a common point.

$$I_t = I_1 + I_2 + I_3$$

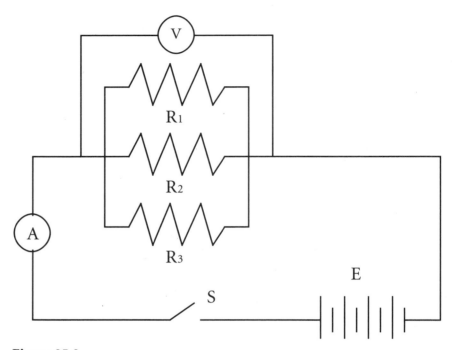

Figure 25.2

The same amount of energy per unit charge will be lost regardless of path between the common points.

$$V_t = V_1 = V_2 = V_3$$

Applying Ohm's Law, the resistance in the parallel network is found by

$$\frac{1}{R_t} = \frac{1}{R_1} + \frac{1}{R_2} + \frac{1}{R_3}$$

In circuits containing both parallel and series paths, the above relationships must apply. Simplification of the circuit can be done to obtain an equivalent resistance and use of Ohm's Law to find the net current delivered to the circuit.

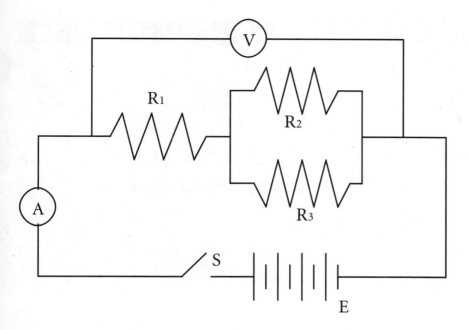

Figure 25.3

In this experiment, you will test the relationships for a simple series circuit and a simple parallel circuit. Then you will apply these relationships to circuits containing resistors in series and parallel combinations.

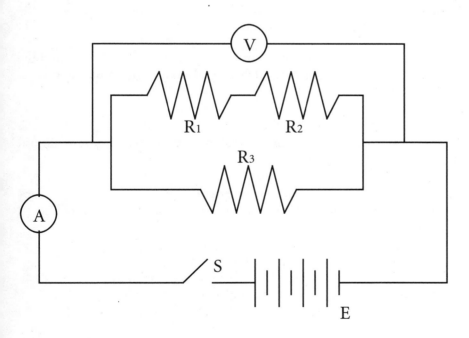

Figure 25.4

After completing this experiment you should be able to do the following:

1. Using the data in the appendix, identify the resistances of each resistor that your instructor has given you, from its color code.

2. Determine the equivalent resistance of several resistors in series or parallel.

3. Determine the equivalent resistance of several resistors in a series-parallel combination.

4. Know how to correctly place ammeters and voltmeters in a circuit.

5. Know that an IR drop in a circuit measures the voltage drop across that part of the circuit.

PROCEDURE

PART A. SERIES NETWORK

Using the three resistances given to you by your instructor, connect the resistors, switch, and power supply as indicated in Fig. 25.1. Correctly place the ammeter in the circuit to measure the current from the source and connect the voltmeter across R_1. When your instructor has approved your circuit, take the reading of the current entering R_1 and the IR drop across the ends of R_1. Record these values in the data.

2. Open the switch, and place the ammeter between R_1 and R_2. Connect the voltmeter across R_2, close the switch and take the readings on the meters. Record your data.

3. Open the switch and place the ammeter between R_2 and R_3. Connect the voltmeter across R_3. Close the switch and quickly take your readings. Record these values in the data table.

4. Open the switch and place the ammeter between R_3 and the power supply. Connect the voltmeter across the series combination of resistors. Record the readings in your data.

5. Is the current through each resistor the same?

5. Calculate the voltage sum and compare it to the value of the source.

Part B. Parallel Network

6. Using three resistances given to you by your instructor, connect the resistors, switch and power supply as indicated in Fig. 25.2. Correctly place the ammeter in the circuit to measure the current from the source and connect the voltmeter across the combination of resistors.

7. Close the switch when your instructor has approved your circuit, and take the ammeter reading for I_t and the voltmeter reading V_t. Record your data in the table under the total for these values.

8. Open the switch and connect the ammeter between the junction and R_1. Place the voltmeter across the ends of R_1. When the meters are correctly inserted in the network, close the switch and take the readings. Record the values in the data table.

9. Open the switch and connect the meters correctly for readings for R_2. Close the switch and record the readings in the data table.

10. Open the switch and connect the meters correctly for readings for R_3. Close the switch and record the readings in the data table.

11. How does the voltage across each resistor compare to the voltage across the source? Calculate the current sum and compare it to the current delivered by the source.

Part C. Series-Parallel Network

12. Using the three resistances given to you by your instructor, connect the resistors, switch and power supply as indicated in Fig. 25.3. Correctly place the ammeter in the circuit to measure the current from the source and connect the voltmeter across the combination of resistors. Close the switch when your instructor has approved your circuit and take the ammeter and voltmeter readings for the entire network. Record your values in the data table.

13. Open the switch and connect the ammeter between R_1 and the junction. Place the voltmeter across the ends of R_1. Close the switch and record your readings.

14. Open the switch and connect the ammeter between the junction and R_2. Place the voltmeter across the ends of R_2. Close the switch and record your readings in the data table. Repeat for R_3.

15. Compare the voltage across R_2 and R_3. Compare the current through R_1 to the sum of that through R_2 and R_3. Is this in accord with the rules for devices in series and parallel?

Part D. Parallel-Series Network

16. Using the three resistances given to you by your instructor, connect the resistors, switch and power supply as indicated in Fig. 25.4. Correctly place the ammeter in the circuit to measure the current from the source and connect the voltmeter across the combination of resistors. Close the switch when your instructor has approved your circuit and take the ammeter and voltmeter readings for the entire network. Record your values in the data table.

17. Open the switch and connect the ammeter between R_1 and R_2. Place the voltmeter across R_1. Close the switch and record your readings.

18. Open the switch and move the voltmeter to read the voltage across R_2. Close the switch and record the readings.

19. Finally open the switch and place the ammeter in series with R_3 and the voltmeter across R_3. Close the switch and record your values.

20. Compare the voltage sum for R_1 and R_2 to the value for R_3. Is this in accord with the rules for devices in series and parallel? Is the current in this network in accord with the rules for devices in series and parallel?

Questions

1. What happens in a series circuit if one of the elements burns out?

2. What happens in a parallel circuit if one of the elements burns out?

3. What would happen to the voltmeter if you did not open the switch before disconnecting it from the circuit?

4. Should elements in a series network be designed to operate at constant current or constant voltage?

5. Should elements in a parallel network be designed to operate at constant current or constant voltage?

Resistors in Series and Parallel

Name: _____   Date: _____

PART A

| Resistor | Resistance R | Current I | Voltage V |
No.	Ω	A	V
R1			
R2			
R3			
RT			

PART B

| Resistor | Resistance R | Current I | Voltage V |
No.	Ω	A	V
R1			
R2			
R3			
RT			

Part C

Resistor	Resistance R	Current I	Voltage V
No.	Ω	A	V
R_1			
R_2			
R_3			
R_T			

Part D

Resistor	Resistance R	Current I	Voltage V
No.	Ω	A	V
R_1			
R_2			
R_3			
R_T			

The Wheatstone Bridge

THEORY

A Wheatstone bridge is a device used for making very precise determinations of resistance. An unknown resistance X is compared to a known resistance using the circuit shown below.

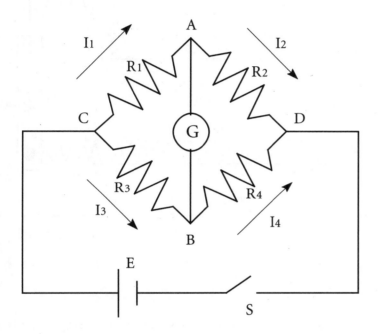

Figure 26.1

Purpose

To measure resistance by the Wheatstone bridge method.

Apparatus

Slide-wire Wheatstone bridge, No. 6 dry cell or other DC power source, galvanometer, plug resistance box or dial resistance box, momentary switch, connecting wires, junction clips, and six 1-watt resistors of varying resistance.

The bridge consists of a network of four resistors, three of which are known and a fourth to be measured. The bridge is balanced when the galvanometer deflection is zero, that is, when there is no current through the galvanometer. This occurs when the potential is exactly the same on both sides of the galvanometer, and the voltage across R_1 is the same as the voltage across R_3. For this condition junctions A and B are at the same potential and $V_{CA} = V_{CB}$. And $V_{AD} = V_{BD}$. The voltage across R_2 will equal the voltage across R_4. In terms of currents and resistances we can write

$$I_1 R_1 = I_3 R_3 \qquad (1)$$

And

$$I_2 R_2 = I_4 R_4 \qquad (2)$$

Source: Puri
Modified by Zober and Zober

With the galvanometer current zero, the current in R_1 is equal to the current in R_2, and the current in R_3 is equal to the current in R_4. Dividing equation (2) by equation (1),

$$\frac{R_2}{R_1} = \frac{R_4}{R_3} \quad \text{and} \quad R_2 = R_1 \frac{R_4}{R_3} \tag{3}$$

In the slide-wire Wheatstone bridge, as in Figure 26.2, the circuit branch CBD is a resistance wire of a metal called manganin 1.00 meter in length.

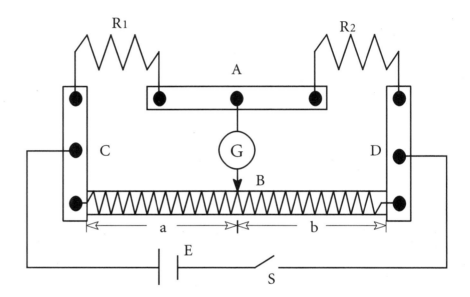

Figure 26.2

The ratio of R_3 to R_4 is the ratio of the two lengths CB to BD. Point A is fixed, and the galvanometer slide-wire contact is moved along CD until the zero point of B is found. A resistance box is used for the known resistance R_1. The working equation becomes

$$R_2 = R_1 \frac{b}{a} \tag{4}$$

After completing this experiment you should be able to do the following:

1. You should be able to determine unknown resistances with precision.

2. Read gauge numbers and calculate the cross sectional area of circular wire.

3. Use a galvanometer in experimental circuit work.

4. Relate resistivity to resistance.

5. Calculate resistivity.

PROCEDURE

1. Arrange the apparatus as shown in Figure 26.2. Check to see if all contact points are clean and shiny. Use lengths of connecting wire as short as possible for all connections. Do not connect the terminals of the battery until the circuit is approved by your instructor. The unknown resistance is R_2, one of the unknown 1-watt resistors and the resistance box is R_1.

2. Unplug or dial in some resistance from the resistance box, momentarily close the switch, and press the slide-wire contact near the 50 cm mark. Allow the switch to remain closed only for short periods of time. As you move the slide-wire contact along the wire mounted to the meterstick watch the galvanometer. Move the slide-wire contact until the meter zeroes. Try to keep the slide-wire contact between 40 and 60 centimeters by adjusting the known resistance.

3. Note the lengths a and b. Use these lengths, the known resistance, R_1, and equation (4) to calculate the unknown resistance. Record this as your experimental resistance. Read the color code on the unknown resistor. You may need to use the color codes in the Appendix. Use this value as your accepted resistance and compare to your experimental value.

4. Repeat procedures 1, 2, and 3 for all of the remaining resistors.

5. If time permits, connect 2 resistors in series and determine the total resistance by using procedures 1, 2, and 3. Do the same with 2 resistors in parallel.

Questions

1. Thermal effects can be a source of error in this experiment. Explain how and why. How can the time period of the switch being closed alter the results of this experiment?

2. Why should you use short pieces of connecting wire in assembling the apparatus for use? Explain.

3. Does the gauge of the connecting wire have any effect on the final results? How?

4. Is this method a more accurate method of determining resistance than that using a voltmeter and ammeter? Explain.

The Wheatstone Bridge

Name: _____   Date: _____

Resistor	R_1	a	b	R_2	Color code R_2
No.	Ω	cm	cm	Ω	Ω
1					
2					
3					
4					
5					
6					

The Electric Equivalent of Heat

THEORY

When a heating coil is placed in a calorimeter containing water and current is applied, electrical energy is converted into thermal energy in the coil. Heat then flows from the coil into the surrounding water causing the temperature of the water and the calorimeter to rise. The principle of energy conservation mandates that the electrical energy developed in the heating coil must equal the thermal energy that appears in the calorimeter system provided that no energy is lost to the system's environment. By measuring the time required to heat the water, the current in the coil, and the potential difference across the coil we can calculate the number of calories per joule, or the mechanical equivalent of heat.

Purpose

To determine the electrical equivalent of heat.

Apparatus

Calorimeter with a 1 to 6 Ω heating coil, stopwatch, DC voltmeter (0 to 7.5 V range), DC ammeter (0 to 10 A range) range, rheostat (10 to 20 Ω range), thermometer, connecting wires, junctions, STSP switch, platform balance and masses, and a 6 V battery or equivalent DC power source.

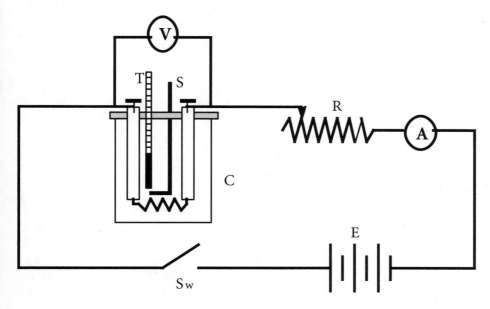

Figure 27.1

The work, W, done transferring a charge, q, across the potential difference of the coil is defined as

$$W = Vq \qquad (1)$$

The total charge transferred is the product of the current, I, and the time, t, or q = It. The work done becomes

$$W = Vq = VIt \qquad (2)$$

The relationship between W, the mechanical or electrical work done in joules and Q, the heat developed in calories due to that work is given by

$$W = QJ \qquad (3)$$

Where J is the proportionality factor known as the *mechanical* or *electrical equivalent of heat*. Solving for J yields

$$J = \frac{W}{Q} = \frac{VIt}{Q} \qquad (4)$$

The value of J may be determined experimentally by measuring the energy put into an isolated system and measuring the increase in the temperature of the system from which the heat input can be calculated. The calorimeter is used to provide the isolated system. The inner cup of the calorimeter containing the heating coil and water is isolated from the environment by the remainder of the calorimeter. The heat produced in the coil warms the water and the calorimeter. If:

m_w = mass, in grams, of water in the calorimeter cup

c_w = specific heat of water = $1.00 \dfrac{cal}{g \cdot C°}$

T_o = initial temperature of the water in °C
T' = final temperature of the water and system in °C

m_s = mass of stirrer
c_s = specific heat of the stirrer
T_o = initial temperature of the stirrer in °C
T' = final temperature of the stirrer and system in °C

mc = mass, in grams, of the calorimeter cup
cc = specific heat of the calorimeter cup
T_T = initial temperature of the calorimeter cup in °C
T' = final temperature of the calorimeter cup and system in °C

All of the components of the system are in thermal equilibrium at T_o, and all of the system's components will have thermal equilibrium, T', at the end of the time period. The heat, Q, gained by the system is found by

$$Q = m_w c_w \Delta T + m_s c_s \Delta T + m_c c_c \Delta T \qquad (5)$$

Factoring yields

$$Q = (m_w c_w + m_s c_s + m_c c_c)\Delta T \qquad (6)$$

The quantity $(m_s c_s + m_w c_w)$ is called *the water equivalent of the calorimeter*. The temperature change in the system is given by $\Delta T = T' - T_o$.

LEARNING OBJECTIVES

After completing this experiment you should be able to do the following:

1. Define the electrical equivalent of heat.

2. State the common units.

3. Show that equation (4) is dimensionally correct.

4. Distinguish between the terms of work and heat.

PROCEDURE

1. Connect the apparatus as shown in Figure 27.1. C is the calorimeter, R the rheostat, Sw the switch, A is the ammeter, V is the voltmeter, and E is the DC power source.

2. The specific heat of the calorimeter cup and stirrer is stamped on the wall of the cup. Record this information.

3. Mass the inner cup of the calorimeter and stirrer. Fill the calorimeter with tap water at about 5°C below room temperature. Fill until it is three-quarters full. Mass the cup and water. Record this in your data.

4. Place the inner cup into the main body of the calorimeter. Cover the calorimeter and insert the thermometer. Stir for 90 seconds to obtain thermal equilibrium. Read the thermometer and record as the initial temperature.

5. Close the switch and start the stopwatch. Read and record the temperature, voltmeter reading, and ammeter reading every 60 seconds thereafter. The rheostat should be adjusted to give a constant 0.5 A. Stir the water gently to distribute the thermal energy in the calorimeter cup.

6. When the thermometer reads a temperature of 10°C above room temperature, open the switch and precisely read the time. Continue stirring until a final equilibrium temperature is reached. Record this temperature.

7. Disassemble the apparatus. Empty the calorimeter and dry it.

8. Plot a graph of temperature vs. time.

9. Use your data in equation (6) to determine the quantity of thermal energy absorbed into the calorimeter system from the heating coil.

10. Determine the electrical equivalent of heat by using equation (4). Compare this to the accepted value of 1 cal = 4.186 J.

QUESTIONS

1. What quantity in this experiment has been measured with the least precision? How might the accuracy of this measurement have been improved?

2. If the experiment had been done with both the initial and final temperatures above room temperature, would the experimental value of J be too high or too low? Explain.

3. If the heating coil of an electric calorimeter is immersed in 500 g of oil of specific heat 0.214 cal/g C° and a steady current of 5.3 A produces a temperature rise of 3.2°C/min, what is the resistance of the coil and the power used in it?

The Electric Equivalent of Heat

Name: _____   Date: _____

Reading No.	Time s	Current I A	Voltage V V	Temperature °C
0				
1				
2				
3				
4				
5				
6				
7				
8				
9				
10				
11				
12				
13				
14				
15				
16				

Mass of calorimeter cup and stirrer   _____ g

Specific heat of cup and stirrer   _____ $\dfrac{\text{cal}}{\text{g} \cdot \text{C}^\circ}$

Mass of cup, stirrer, and water   _____ g

Mass of the water, m_w _____ g

Average voltage reading, V   _____ V

Average current reading, I   _____ A

Initial temperature of the system   _____ °C

Final temperature of the system   _____ °C

Temperature change, ΔT _____ C°

Total time of heating, t   _____ s

Heat gained by the system, Q   _____ cal

Energy input, W   _____ J

Experimental electrical equivalent of heat, J   _____ $\dfrac{\text{J}}{\text{cal}}$

Accepted electrical equivalent of heat, J   _____ $\dfrac{\text{J}}{\text{cal}}$

Error   _____ $\dfrac{\text{J}}{\text{cal}}$

% Error   _____ %

Snell's Law

THEORY

When light passes obliquely from a medium of smaller optical density into a medium of greater optical density part of the ray is reflected and part is refracted, bending toward the normal in the medium of greater optical density. This bending or refraction happens because there is an abrupt change of speed at the interface between the media. The velocity of the light decreases, its frequency remains constant meaning that its wavelength will become smaller. If the ray of light enters the boundary along the normal, its speed will change, but there will be no bending.

The ratio of the speed of light in a medium, v, to the speed of light in air (vacuum), c, is called the index of refraction.

$$n = \frac{c}{v}$$

The angle of incidence is θ_1 and the angle of refraction, which depends on the speed of light in the medium, is θ_2

$$n_1 \sin \theta_1 = n_2 \sin \theta_2$$

In vacuum we take the index of refraction to be exactly 1, and in air at STP conditions it is 1.00029, close enough to 1 that we use 1 in calculations. Nothing has an index of refraction less than 1.

We will not deal with total internal reflection in this laboratory experiment.

Purpose

To study Snell's law and determine the speed of light in water and ethanol.

Apparatus

Semi-circular optical box, straight pins, ruler, cardboard, polar coordinate paper, water, and ethanol.

LEARNING OBJECTIVES

After completing this experiment you should be able to do the following:

1. Define the term index of refraction.

2. Calculate the speed of light in a medium if you know its index of refraction.

3. Determine the angle of refraction in a given medium if you know the angle of incidence and the index of refraction for that medium.

4. Know the speed of light is greatest in a vacuum.

5. Make a diagram for the interface between two media, showing the angles of incidence and reflection for the upper surface and the angle of refraction in the denser medium.

Procedure

1. Make a vertical mark in the center of the flat side of the optical box.

2. Place the polar coordinate paper on top of the cardboard. Align the flat edge of the optical box along the 0°—180° line on the coordinate paper with its center aligned with the 90°—270° line. Fill the box slightly more than three-quarters full of water.

3. Stick a pin, no more than 4 cm, away from the flat surface of the box along the 90°—270° line. Look at the pin through the water from the curved side of the box and move your head slightly until you can line up the pin and the vertical mark on the box. Mark this line of sight position on the coordinate paper on the curved side of the box.

4. Change the position of the pin on the flat side of the box to obtain an angle of 10° with the normal. Line up the pin and the vertical mark as you did in the above step.

5. Continue for angles of incidence up in 10° increments to 70°.

6. Carefully read the pin marks from the polar coordinate paper and transfer these readings to your data sheet.

7. Calculate the index of refraction for each trial and determine the average value.

8. Plot a graph of $\dfrac{\sin \theta_1}{\sin \theta_2}$ vs. θ_1

9. Calculate the speed of light for water and determine your percent difference.

10. Repeat the experiment using ethanol as the medium in the optical box.

Questions

1. What happens to the ray of light as it passes from air to water if it travels along the normal?

2. Why did you not include the bending of light as it passed through the walls of the container in your calculation?

3. A 680nm light ray enters water. What is the velocity of light in water? What is the frequency of the light in water? What is the wavelength of light in the water?

Snell's Law

Name: _____   Date: _____

Data block for water:

Angle of incidence	Angle of refraction	$\sin\theta_i$	$\sin\theta_r$	$\dfrac{\sin\theta_i}{\sin\theta_r}$
θ_i	θ_r	—	—	—
0°				
10°				
20°				
30°				
40°				
50°				
60°				
70°				

Data block for ethanol:

Angle of incidence	Angle of refraction	$\sin\theta_i$	$\sin\theta_r$	$\dfrac{\sin\theta_i}{\sin\theta_r}$
θ_i	θ_r	—	—	—
0°				
10°				
20°				
30°				
40°				
50°				
60°				
70°				

Lenses

THEORY

A thin lens has two refracting surfaces that are sections of a spherical surface. Light may pass through the lens in two directions, resulting in focal points on either side of the lens.

The *focal length f* of the lens is measured from the optical center of the lens to either focus. The focal length does not equal half of the radius curvature as a mirror does; it depends rather on the index of refraction of the material of lens and the radius of curvature of both parts of the spherical lens.

Image formation for a lens can be determined by ray diagrams or by an analytical method. The analytical method determines the image position and type by use of the lens equation,

$$\frac{1}{f} = \frac{1}{p} + \frac{1}{q} \tag{1}$$

where f is the focal length. (The focal length is positive for a converging lens and negative for a diverging lens.) The object distance, p, and the image distance, q, are considered to be positive for real objects and real images—real images are located on the opposite side of the lens. The distances are considered to be negative for virtual objects and images. A virtual image is formed on the same side of the lens as the object.

The magnification of the image is given by the equations listed below. A positive magnification will indicate that the image is erect and virtual.

$$M = \frac{-q}{p} \tag{2}$$

Or,

$$M = \frac{h'}{h} \tag{3}$$

Ray diagrams used to locate the image utilize ray-tracing methods similar to those used for mirrors.

1. A ray of light passing through the optical center of the lens will not deviate from its path.

2. A ray of light parallel to the principal axis (the principal axis is a line drawn through both foci and the optical center of the lens.) will pass through

Source: Puri
Modified by Zober and Zober

Purpose

To determine the focal length of convex lenses.

Apparatus

Optical bench, with light source and sliding mounts, several convex lenses, object (slit in a metal plate in the form of an arrow), screen, and a cm ruler.

the focal point on the opposite side of the lens. It will appear to come from the focal point on the near side of the lens for a diverging (negative lens).

3. A ray of light passing through the focal point on the near side of a converging lens is refracted parallel to the principal axis. For a diverging lens, this ray proceeds to the second focal point of the lens.

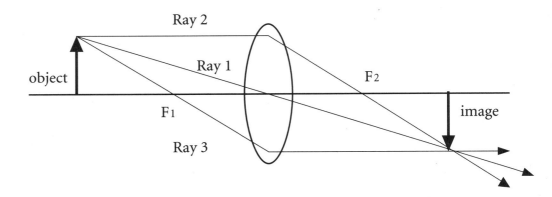

Figure 29

LEARNING OBJECTIVES

After completing this experiment you should be able to do the following:

1. Distinguish between a converging and a diverging lens.

2. Differentiate between real and virtual images.

3. Construct a ray diagram for the formation of an image.

4. Solve for an unknown parameter in the thin lens equation.

5. Calculate the magnification of an image.

PROCEDURE

Part of this experiment is to design your own data sheets. Study the procedures to decide how you will do these data sheets.

1. Measure the size of the arrow or the tip of the arrow and record this value in your data table as h.

2. Place the object, the arrow, into the sliding mount, and position it in front of the light source. The slit will transmit light from the source (form of an arrow) and help to collimate the light source on the bench.

3. Place a double convex lens into a sliding holder and position it on the bench, 20 cm in front of the object.

4. Place the screen into a sliding holder and by moving it back and forth; find a position on the bench where the image of the arrow is sharply defined. Measure the distance, p, between the object and the lenses. Record this distance in your data table. Measure the distance, q, between the lens and the image and record this distance in your data table. Measure the size of the image, h', (in the same manner that you had measured the object), and record its size in your data table.

5. Is the image real or virtual, inverted or erect? Record in your data table.

6. Calculate the focal length of the lens using equation (1) and record in your data table.

7. Calculate the magnification of the image using equations (2) and (3). Compare these magnifications.

8. Repeat the procedures 4 to 7 for 5 additional readings of object and image positions. Use a wide range of object distances in these readings.

9. Average the focal lengths for your trials. Obtain the correct value for the focal length of the lens from your instructor and determine your error and percent error.

10. Plot a graph of $\dfrac{1}{q}$ vs. $\dfrac{1}{p}$ using your experimental data. What does the shape of the line suggest?

11. Repeat the experiment for a second lens.

QUESTIONS

1. Make a ray diagram of one of your trials, showing the image formation for the lens.

2. What type of image is produced when the object is placed at (a) 2f, (b) f and (c) < f.

3. Can you make a lens from a drop of water? Could you use it to magnify objects?

4. Investigate the lens maker's equation.

5. A converging lens produces an upright image with a magnification of +3 when it is placed 10 cm from an object. What is the focal length of the lens?

Lenses

Name: _____   Date: _____

Trial	Object distance p	Image distance q	Focal length f
No.	cm	cm	cm
1			
2			
3			
4			
5			
6			

Trial	Object height h	Image height h´	Magnification M	Magnification M
No.	cm	cm	$\dfrac{h'}{h}$	$\dfrac{-q}{p}$
1				
2				
3				
4				
5				
6				

The Compound Microscope

THEORY

The microscope is a useful tool in many professions. The design of a high quality microscope can be quite complex, involving compound lenses and intricate lens coatings. But the complexity arises primarily from the need to reduce the effects of aberrations, notably spherical and chromatic aberrations.

The basic optical theory behind the microscope is simple and its application is straightforward. It requires only the understanding of the **Fundamental Lens Equation** (thin lens formula):

$$\frac{1}{s} + \frac{1}{s'} = \frac{1}{f} \tag{1}$$

for which the magnification of the image is given by the equation;

$$m = -\frac{s'}{s} \tag{2}$$

where s is the *object distance*, s' is the *image distance*, f is the *focal length* and m is the *magnification* of the image. The magnification is **positive** for erect images and **negative** for inverted images. Recall that in the "all +" convention;

$s > 0$, for *real objects* and $s < 0$, for *virtual objects,*

$s' > 0$, for *real images* and $s' < 0$, for *virtual images.*

The magnification of the objective lens (m_o) can be fixed by adjusting the object distance (s_o) and the image distance (s'_o) of the lens. From the Fundamental Lens Equations [Eq. (1) and (2)], solving for s_o and s'_o in terms of m_o and f_o (focal length of objective lens), we get;

$$m_o = -\frac{s'_o}{s_o} = -s'_o\left(\frac{1}{f_o} - \frac{1}{s'_o}\right) \tag{3}$$

or

$$s'_o = f_o(1 - m_o) \tag{4}$$

Again,

$$s_o = f_o\frac{(m_o - 1)}{m} \tag{5}$$

Source: Ramirez
Modifed by Zober and Zober

Experiment Thirty

Purpose

To demonstrate the construction of a compound microscope and determine the magnification of the final image.

Apparatus

Optical bench; incandescent light source; component holders (3); variable aperture; crossed arrow target; viewing screen; +75 mm focal length convex lens; +150 mm focal length convex lens.

In our microscope, we shall initially take $m_o = -2$ (an inverted image magnified 2 times). Then s_o and s'_o will be both positive and real.

The magnification of the eyepiece, m_e, will be fixed by f_e (the focal length of the eyepiece) and the fact that s'_e (the distance of the image, seen by the eye) should be about -22 cm. This distance (-22 cm) is a limitation of the human eye. There is a distance, called the near point, at which the image in front of the eye begins to blur, because the rays entering the eye from the object are too divergent for the eye to focus. (To see this, hold an object at arms length and move it slowly towards one eye, with the other eye closed).

The magnification of the eyepiece, m_e, is again calculated from the Fundamental Lens Equations (1). That is:

$$\frac{1}{s_e} + \frac{1}{s'_e} = \frac{1}{f_e} \tag{6}$$

Multiplying by s'_e, we get,

$$\frac{s'_e}{s_e} + \frac{1}{1} = \frac{s'_e}{f_e}. \tag{7}$$

Using Equation (2), we get,

$$m_e = 1 - \frac{s'_e}{f_e} = 1 + \frac{22cm}{f_e} \tag{8}$$

LEARNING OBJECTIVES

After completing the experiment you should be able to do the following:

1. Explain in words or with a diagram, the basic theory behind the construction of a microscope.

2. Define near and far points for the human eye.

3. Define spherical aberration and chromatic aberration.

4. Determine the magnification of the objective lens.

5. Determine the magnification of the eyepiece.

PROCEDURE

Before beginning, identify each item of the apparatus you will be using.

I. In the introduction, it was mentioned that the distance of most distinct vision (called the near point) was 22 cm. This near point differs for different people. Verify this, by holding the Viewing Screen in your hand at arms length, and observing some fine detail on it (the centimeter scale), while moving it slowly towards your *right eye* (left eye closed) until the detail is focused. Repeat this with the *left eye* (right eye closed).

Now, ask your partner to repeat this procedure, and then calculate the average distance.

*The objective (L_1) is the lens with the **shorter** focal length ($f_o = +75$ mm). The eyepiece (L_2) is the lens with the **longer** focal length ($f_e = +150$ mm).*

2. Measure (verify) the focal length of each lens, f_o and f_e (Distance between object and image screen greater that $4f$ of lens). Measure the diameter (D) of each lens, and record their *f*-stop

$$f_{stop} = \frac{f}{D}$$

3. (a) Using Eq. (4) and (5), calculate the image distance, s'_o and the object distance, s_o, for an image magnification, $m_o = -2$, for the objective lens.

(b) Set up the components, with distances s'_o and s_o, as calculated above, (3a) (see Fig. 30.1). Verify this result, by first measuring the diameter of the circle on the Crossed Arrow Target, with the meter scale and then the diameter of the circle of the image on the Viewing Screen with the scale. Is the magnification of the image 2 times that of the object?

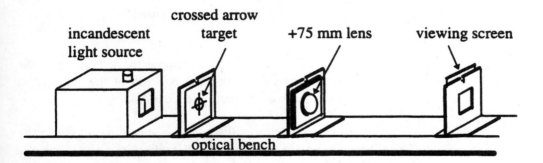

Figure 30.1

4. Using Eq. (8), determine the magnification of the eyepiece, m_e. Using this value, calculate the distance s_e. The distance between the objective and the eyepiece of the microscope will be $(s'_o + s_e)$. (See Fig. 30.2.)

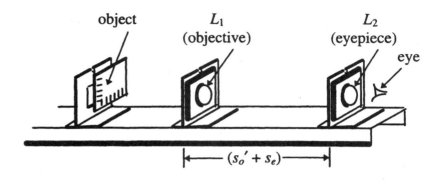

Figure 30.2

5. Set up the microscope as shown in Figure 30.2. [Note: Switch OFF the light source on the Optical Bench.] Use the +75 mm focal length as the objective lens and the +150 mm focal length as the eyepiece. The object is the *scale* of the Viewing Screen.

Place the eyepiece close to the edge of the Optical Bench and then place the Bench itself at the edge of the table, so that you can position your eye close to the eyepiece.

Use the calculated values from steps (3) and (4), of the image and object distances for both the lenses, and construct the microscope (use Fig. 30.1 as a reference). Is the image magnified when you look through the eyepiece?

Now position the objective lens approximately 14 cm from the Viewing Screen (the object). Adjust the position of the eyepiece (while looking through it with one eye), until you see a clearly focused image of the Viewing Screen scale.

Look through the eyepiece and slowly move the objective lens closer to the Viewing Screen at 2 cm intervals. Adjust the position of the eyepiece as needed, at each interval, to retain the best possible focus.

Note the increase in magnification as the objective lens moves closer to the object. This is because the projected image of the object increases in magnification, as the distance between object and objective gets closer to the focal length of the lens. (Figs. 30.1 and 30.2.) The image will be lost entirely when the objective is 75 mm from the object, *i.e.* at the focal point. Verify this.

Focusing problems also start to develop as the magnification increases. Spherical and chromatic aberrations become significant at very high magnifications.

Attach the Variable Aperture to the other side of the Component Holder with the objective lens and facing the object, to restrict the path of light to the central regions of the objective lens.

Begin with the Variable Aperture *fully open* and the objective lens 10 cm from the object (Viewing Screen). While looking through the eyepiece at the *focused* image, collapse the aperture plates from both directions, until the aperture size is about 2-3 mm. (Be sure that the V formed by the two aperture plates is centered on the notch at the top of the Component Holder).

Refer to the DATA section when answering the following questions.

What effect does the size of the aperture have on the spherical aberration?

What effect does the size of the aperture have on the brightness of the image?

6. The *theoretical total magnification, $m_t = m_o \times m_e$.* For our microscope, we fixed $m_o = -2$, and m_e was calculated from Equation (8) with $f_e = 150$ mm.

Using $m_o = -2$, calculate m_e, using the value of f_e (average) found in Calculation (2). Hence calculate the *experimental total magnification $m_{t(exp)}$.*

QUESTIONS

1. Compare your average distance of the most distinct vision with the given value of 22 cm.

2. Chromatic aberrations become significant at high magnifications. What colors are evident?

3. Compare the experimental and theoretical total magnifications obtained. Explain any discrepancies.

The Compound Microscope

Name: _____   Lab Partners: _____

Date: _____

I. DATA

(1) Distance to hand (*right eye*) = _____

   Distance to hand (*left eye*) = _____

   Distance to hand (*partner's right eye*) = _____

   Distance to hand (*partner's left eye*) = _____

   Average distance = _____

(2) For lens 1 (**+75 mm lens**)

   a) Image *smaller* than object

   Position of lamp = _____

   Position of lens = _____

   Position of image = _____

   $s = $ _____ − _____ = _____

   $s' = $ _____ − _____ = _____

   b) Image *larger* than object

   Position of lamp = _____

   Position of lens = _____

   Position of image = _____

   $s = $ _____ − _____ = _____

   $s' = $ _____ − _____ = _____

c) Diameter of lens 1 = _____

For lens 2 (**+150 mm lens**)

a) Image *smaller* than object

   Position of lamp = _____

   Position of lens = _____

   Position of image = _____

$s = $ _____ − _____ = _____

$s' = $ _____ − _____ = _____

b) Image *larger* than object

   Position of lamp = _____

   Position of lens = _____

   Position of image = _____

$s = $ _____ − _____ = _____

$s' = $ _____ − _____ = _____

c) Diameter of lens 2 = _____

(3) a) Use $m_o = -2$

   $s'_o = f_o(1 - m_o) = $ _____

   $s_o = \dfrac{f_o(m_o - 1)}{m_o} = $ _____

b) Experimental verification

   Position of lamp = _____

   Position of lens = _____

   Position of image = _____

$s_o = $ _____ − _____ = _____

$s'_o = $ _____ − _____ = _____

(3) Use $s'_o = -22$ cm

$$m_e = 1 - \left(\frac{s'_e}{f_e}\right) = \underline{\hspace{5cm}}$$

$$s_e = -\left(\frac{s'_e}{m_e}\right) = \underline{\hspace{5cm}}$$

Calculated magnification $= \dfrac{\text{Diameter of circle of Target}}{\text{Diameter of circle of Image}} = \underline{\hspace{4cm}}$

(5) Effect of size of the aperture on:

(a) Spherical aberration.

(b) Brightness of image.

II. CALCULATIONS

(2) For lens 1

$$\frac{1}{f} = \frac{1}{s'} + \frac{1}{s}$$

(a) $f_a = \underline{\hspace{5cm}}$

(b) $f_b = \underline{\hspace{5cm}}$

Average, $\bar{f}_o = \dfrac{(f_a + f_b)}{2} = \underline{\hspace{5cm}}$

For lens 2

(a) $f_a = \underline{\hspace{3cm}}$

(b) $f_b = \underline{\hspace{3cm}}$

Average, $\bar{f}_e = \dfrac{(f_a + f_b)}{2} = \underline{\hspace{5cm}}$

The objective should have the *shorter* focal length and the eyepiece the *longer* length.

$f_o = \underline{\hspace{5cm}}$ $\qquad$ $f_e = \underline{\hspace{5cm}}$

$$f\text{-stop} = \frac{f}{D}$$

$f_o\text{-stop} = \underline{\hspace{3.5cm}}$ $\qquad$ $f_e\text{-stop} = \underline{\hspace{5cm}}$

(4) Using s_o' and s_e, find the distance between the lens of the compound microscope. [Hint: See Procedure (4).]

(5) Sketch the experimental set-up (basically Fig. 30.2), labeling the lenses (objective and eyepiece), the images and the distances of the microscope (focal lengths, image and object distances).

(6) Compute the *theoretical total magnification,*

$m_t = m_o \times m_e = $ _____

Compute the *experimental total magnification,*

$m_{t(exp)} = m_o \times m_e = $ _____

Diffraction

THEORY

The deviation of light from its original path as it passes through a narrow opening or around an obstruction is called *diffraction*. Interference patterns are evidence of the diffraction of light.

Monochromatic light passing through a single slit of some width a, will produce an interference pattern on a screen placed a distance L away. The interference pattern will show a bright central maximum (m = 0) and a number of dark fringes produced by destructive interference at a distance y on either side of the central maximum. The equation for this destructive interference is given by

$$a \sin \theta = m\lambda \quad \text{where} \quad \sin \theta = \frac{y}{L} \tag{1}$$

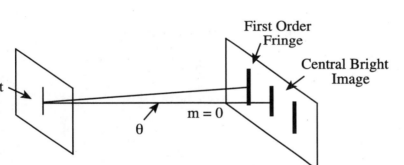

First Order Fringe

Central Bright Image

Slit

m = 0

θ

Figure 31.1

Double slit interference patterns produce a central maximum by constructive interference of the light from the two slits and secondary bright maxima when the path difference is $m\lambda$. A path difference of $\dfrac{m\lambda}{2}$ will produce a dark fringe.

Source: Puri
Modified by Zober

Purpose

To determine the wavelength of a coherent light source, the laser, by means of a diffraction grating.

Apparatus

Various diffraction gratings, diffraction grating holder, He-Ne laser, and a meter-stick.

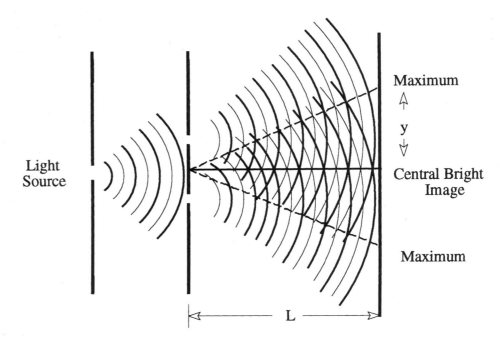

Light
Source

Maximum

y

Central Bright
Image

Maximum

L

Figure 31.2

The equation for constructive interference is

$$d \sin \theta = m\lambda \qquad (2)$$

where d is the distance between the two slits.
And,

$$y_{bright} = \frac{m\lambda L}{d}$$

A diffraction grating is ruled with a large number of closely spaced parallel slits that are a few wavelengths apart. The space between the lines will transmit the light if the grating is glass or a colloid. It will reflect the light if it is a metal grating. Your CD's are a good example of a reflective grating. The ruled spaces reflect the light diffusely, thus their light not a factor in the diffraction process

White light passing through the grating will be separated into sharp spectra on either side of the white central image. The light from the laser, passing through the grating will give a central maxima and a number of secondary maxima. The number of orders depends on the wavelength of the light and the spacing of the lines. The interference pattern produced can be evaluated for maxima by the same equation that is used for the interference pattern produced from double slits.

$$d \sin \theta = m\lambda$$

And, $d = \dfrac{1}{N}$ where N is the number of lines per ruling.

LEARNING OBJECTIVES

After completing this lab you will be able to do the following:

1. Define diffraction.

2. Explain what is meant by the interference of light.

3. Explain the difference between a transmission grating and a reflection grating.

4. Determine the spacing between the lines on a diffraction grating.

5. Calculate the wavelength of light used in the experiment.

PROCEDURE

1. Determine the spacing of the diffraction gratings. Record these values in you data table.

2. Place the diffraction grating with the smallest ruling in the holder, and place it 30 cm in front of the laser.

3. Measure the distance from the diffraction grating to the screen. This should be at least 1.5 m. Record the distance.

4. Turn on the laser. (NEVER LOOK AT THE LASER DIRECTLY!) Adjust the holder if necessary. The light from the laser should pass through the center of the grating.

5. How many orders do you see?

6. Measure the distance from the central image to the first order at the right of it (m = 1) and the first order at the left of it (m = −1) Record both distances. Average these two values and record.

7. Measure the distance from the central image to the second order to the right and left of the central image. Again, record the distances and the average distance.

8. Repeat for the third order spectra.

9. Calculate the wavelength of the transmitted light for each of the three orders and determine your percentage error. The wavelength of the He-Ne laser is 632.8 nm.

10. Repeat procedures 5 to 9 for other diffraction gratings. What happens to the pattern as you switch gratings?

11. Which order is most accurate in determining the wavelength of light? Why?

QUESTIONS

1. Is the separation of the orders greater or smaller for a diffraction grating with many lines?

2. If white light is used in an experiment, will there be a greater separation of red and blue light in the first-order spectra or in the second-order spectra.

3. Why does the number of orders depend on the wavelength and the spacing of the lines?

4. Which spectra will be more sharply defined, first-order spectra or a third-order spectra? Why?

Diffraction

Name: _____ Date: _____

Grating _____ N _____ L _____ $\frac{1}{d}$ _____

maxima	y_{bright} right	y_{bright} left	Average y	Wavelength λ
—	cm	cm	cm	nm
m = 1				
m = 2				
m = 3				

Grating _____ N _____ L _____ $\frac{1}{d}$ _____

maxima	y_{bright} right	y_{bright} left	Average y	Wavelength λ
—	cm	cm	cm	nm
m = 1				
m = 2				
m = 3				

Grating _____ N _____ L _____ $\dfrac{1}{d}$ _____

maxima	y_{bright} right	y_{bright} left	Average y	Wavelength λ
—	cm	cm	cm	nm
m = 1				
m = 2				
m = 3				

Grating _____ N _____ L _____ $\dfrac{1}{d}$ _____

maxima	y_{bright} right	y_{bright} left	Average y	Wavelength λ
—	cm	cm	cm	nm
m = 1				
m = 2				
m = 3				

Charge on an Electron

THEORY

In a classic experiment in 1909, Robert A. Millikan established the existence of the elementary unit of electrical charge, the electron. His experiment consisted of measuring the velocity of the charged microscopic oil drops as they moved between the plates of a parallel plate capacitor. During his experiment, the charged oil droplet was subjected to three different types of forces: gravitational force, electrical force, and a frictional force due to the charged body's motion through air.

If no external electric field, E, exists between the plates then the net force acting on the drops is due to gravity and the frictional force arising from their passage though the air, then

$$\sum F = ma = mg - kv_t = 0 \qquad (1)$$

Where m is the mass of the drop, g the acceleration due to gravity, k the frictional force proportionally constant for air, and v_t is the terminal velocity of the drop in free fall. Because the spheres are small, they reach terminal velocity quickly.

If the charge is placed in an electric field, E, an electrical force is exerted on the charge of magnitude q, by

$$F = qE \qquad (2)$$

and the resulting force acting on the drop when terminal velocity is reached, is then given by

$$\sum F = ma = qE - mg - kv_e = 0 \qquad (3)$$

where v_e is the terminal velocity of the drop arising when the electric field is applied in the direction opposite to the gravitational field. Combining equation (1) and (3)

$$qE - mg - kv_e = 0$$

transposing

$$qE = mg + kv_e$$

Now

$$mg = kv_t$$

Source: Puri
Modified by Zober and Zober

Purpose

To determine the charge on the electron by the Millikan method.

Apparatus

Millikan apparatus, dual power supply (0 to 300 V DC, 30 ma and 6.3 Volts AC, 2 Amp), DC voltmeter, 0 to 200 V range, latex spheres, connecting wires, and a stopwatch.

Substituting gives

$$qE = kv_t + kv_e$$

Factoring,

$$qE = k(v_t + v_e)$$

Finally substituting for k,

$$k = \frac{mg}{v_t}$$

Gives,

$$q = ne = \frac{mg}{E}\left(\frac{v_e + v_t}{v_t}\right) \qquad (5)$$

Here,
    n is the number of electric charges
    e is the magnitude of the electronic charge
    E is the electric field strength in $\frac{V}{m}$
    v_t is the terminal velocity in free fall
    v_e is the terminal velocity when an electric field is applied.

The electrical field strength may be determined if the voltage V across the capacitor, and the plate separation d, are known

$$E = \frac{V}{d} \qquad (6)$$

In this experiment, we will use microscopic latex spheres of uniform diameter and mass instead of oil droplets that may be of any size.

LEARNING OBJECTIVES

After completing this experiment you should be able to do the following:

1. Know that the fundamental unit of charge is 1.60×10^{-19} C.

2. Know that charge is quantized, that is, they are some whole number times the fundamental unit of charge.

3. Recognize that three forces act on the charge; the force of gravity, the electrical force, and the frictional force. The net force therefore determines the motion of the charge.

4. Calculate the electrical field strength between the plates of the capacitor.

PROCEDURE

1. Calculate the mass of the latex spheres. The density of the spheres is 1.05 $\frac{g}{cm^3}$ and the mean diameter of the spheres generally ranges from 900nm to 1100 nm. (Check the bottle of spheres that you are using for this experiment to obtain the correct diameter.)

2. Your instructor should have already focused the telescope and light source and the apparatus should be in operating condition. Any adjustment that you might make to improve your field of view should be a minor one.

3. Set the voltmeter to 100 V and place the toggle switch in the center. The capacitor plates are shorted when the switch is in this position and no electrical field exists in the region between the plates. Squeeze the bulb to introduce spheres into the region between the capacitor plates. (You may have to squeeze the bulb several times to do this.) The bright spots that you see appear to be rising because the telescope inverts the field of view. They are actually falling. Do all the spheres move in the same direction? Are they accelerating as they move across the field of view or are they moving slowly?

4. Select a sphere and observe what happens as you apply a voltage of 100 volts. How do they move when the toggle is up? How do they move when the toggle is down? Do all of the spheres have the same sign of charge? Do all spheres have the same magnitude of charge?

5. Spheres that have a large charge can be easily swept out of the field, leaving the particles we wish to investigate remaining in the field for long times. By switching the polarity we can drive the charge up or down, maintaining the same charge in the field of view.

PART I.

6. Introduce additional spheres into the chamber, selecting a slow moving charge. Time this charge over two parts of the field (grid will be visible) with the plates shorted. Record the time. Apply a voltage and bring the charge "down" to the bottom of the grid. Time the charge over two parts of the field—record the time. Make another reading of the *same charge* over two parts of the field and record the time.

7. Apply an electric field and time the *same charge* as it moves slowly "downward" over two parts of the field. Record the time, the voltage, and the polarity of the voltage. Repeat for two more timings for the same charge. Record the time. (Do not change the voltage as you do this, only toggle the switch to control the movement of the charge.)

8. Make three sets of observations of a sphere following procedures 6 and 7.

9. Ask you instructor for the plate separation d, it should be around 5 mm. Knowing the number of divisions of the grid, you can calculate E, v_t, and v_e for this procedure. Calculate the charge on the sphere for each set of observations. Compare to the basic unit of charge.

PART II.

10. Adjust the voltage producing the electric field to one that will balance the gravitational field. Knowing $F = Eq$ and $F = mg$ we will balance the forces on the charge so it is stationary. This will happens when

$$eq = mg$$

Since

$$E = \frac{V}{d}$$

Then,

$$q = \frac{mgd}{V} \tag{7}$$

mgd a constant for this experiment making $q \propto \dfrac{1}{V}$

11. Squeeze additional charge into the region between the plate; select a slow moving charge. Toggle the switch to control the polarity of the voltage and adjust the voltage until the charge is stationary in the vertical direction. Record the voltage. Calculate q from equation (7).

12. Repeat this part of the procedure until you have a total of 15 readings obtained by adjusting the voltage until the charge is stationary. The majority of your readings will be in the 75 to 200 V range. See if you can obtain a stationary charge with a voltage above 200 V.

13. After you have determined the charge on each of your 15 stationary charges, see if quantization is indicated. What is your basic unit of charge? How does it compare with the accepted value of 1.60×10^{-19} C?

QUESTIONS

1. Which part was more accurate in determining a fundamental unit of charge? Explain.

2. If your voltmeter gave a value that was 10 V too high, how would it affect your results?

3. Is there any evidence that latex spheres could have clumped together in this experiment?

4. Show that a $\frac{V}{m}$ is equivalent to a $\frac{N}{C}$.

Charge on the Electron

PART I

Charge q_1: Voltage_____   Distance between plates _____

Trial	Distance	Time	Terminal Velocity V_t	Distance	Time	Terminal Velocity V_e
1						
2						
3						

Charge q_2: Voltage_____   Distance between plates _____

Trial	Distance	Time	Terminal Velocity V_t	Distance	Time	Terminal Velocity V_e
1						
2						
3						

Charge q_3: Voltage_____   Distance between plates _____

Trial	Distance	Time	Terminal Velocity V_t	Distance	Time	Terminal Velocity V_e
1						
2						
3						

PART II

mg _____   mgd _____

Trial No.	Voltage V	$q = \dfrac{mgd}{V}$
1		
2		
3		
4		
5		
6		
7		
8		
9		
10		
11		
12		
13		
14		
15		

The Spectrum of Hydrogen and Planck's Constant

THEORY

The diffraction grating spectrometer is an instrument that is used to determine the wavelengths of spectral lines. The diffraction grating consists of several thousand equally spaced parallel slits per cm or mm ruled on a glass surface. When light passes through a diffraction grating, it is diffracted by the individual slits, forming an interference pattern. Constructive interference occurs when the path difference between adjacent slits is λ, 2λ, 3λ, ... where λ is the wavelength. When the grating is normal to the incident light, the grating equation is

$$n\lambda = d \sin \theta \tag{1}$$

where n is the order of the spectrum, d is the grating slit spacing, and θ is the angle between the rays forming the line in question and the normal to the grating.

The diffraction grating spectrometer is an instrument used to determine the wavelengths of various elements since each element emits a characteristic pattern of discrete wavelengths. These wavelengths correspond to the absorption and release of discrete amounts of energy.

The Swiss physicist J.J. Balmer discovered a simple empirical relationship between the wavelengths of visible light emitted in the hydrogen spectrum. This relationship is given by

$$\frac{1}{\lambda} = R\left[\frac{1}{2^2} - \frac{1}{n^2}\right]$$

Where $n = 3, 4, 5, \ldots$ and R is a constant called the *Rydberg Constant* which has a value of $1.097 \times 10^7 m^{-1}$. Similar relationships occur in the ultraviolet and the infrared parts of the spectrum.

In 1913 Niels Bohr gave an explanation of these spectral lines. According to the Bohr theory, whenever the energy of the atom changes from an initial value of E_i to a final value of E_f, the atom emits radiation of frequency, given by

$$f = \frac{E_i - E_f}{h} \tag{2}$$

Source: Puri
Modified by Zober and Zober

Experiment Thirty-three

Purpose

(a) To calibrate and use a diffraction grating spectrometer, (b) to determine the wavelengths of the spectral lines of atomic hydrogen, and (c) to calculate Plank's constant.

Apparatus

Diffraction grating spectrometer, mercury light source, hydrogen spectrum tube, power supply and lead wires.

where E_i and E_f are initial and final energies of the atom before and after the emission of a photon of frequency f, and h is *Planck's* constant. The relationship between the wavelength λ and the frequency of a photon is given by

$$f = \frac{c}{\lambda} \tag{3}$$

Bohr showed that the energy of the initial and the final states of an atom is given by

$$E_i = \left[\frac{-2\pi^2 k^2 m e^4}{h^2} \right] \cdot \frac{1}{n_i^2} \quad \text{and} \quad E_f = \left[\frac{-2\pi^2 k^2 m e^4}{h^2} \right] \cdot \frac{1}{n_f^2}$$

Combining equations 2, 3, 4, and 5 gives the wavelengths of the Balmer series as

$$\frac{1}{\lambda} = \frac{2\pi^2 k^2 m e^4}{h^3 c} \left[\frac{1}{n_f^2} - \frac{1}{n_1^2} \right] \tag{4}$$

Where $n_f = 2$ and $n_i = 3, 4, 5, \ldots, \infty$.

The Rydberg Constant is then:

$$R = \frac{2\pi^2 k^2 m e^4}{h^3 c} \tag{5}$$

The prominent lines in the Balmer or hydrogen series are:

$H_\alpha = 656\ nm$
$H_\beta = 486.1\ nm$
$H_\gamma = 434.1\ nm$

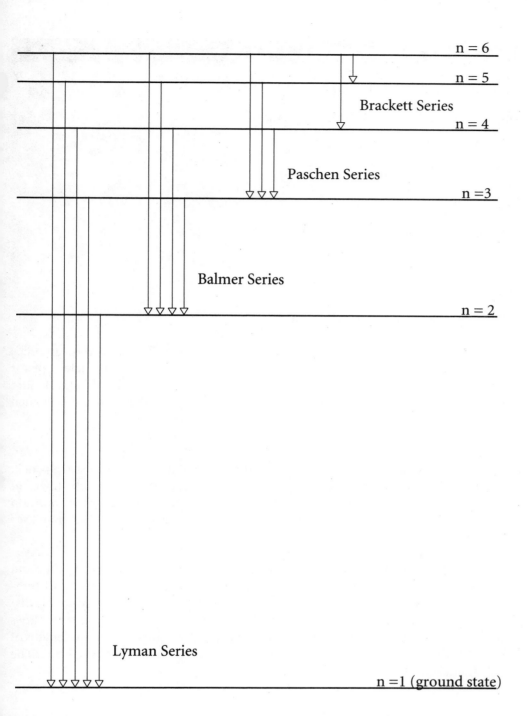

n = 6

n = 5

Brackett Series

n = 4

Paschen Series

n = 3

Balmer Series

n = 2

Lyman Series

n = 1 (ground state)

Figure 33.1

After completing the experiment, you should be able to do the following:

1. Calculate the spacing between the lines of a diffraction grating.

2. Calculate the wavelength of the spectral lines.

3. Calculate the frequency of the spectral line.

4. Calculate the energy transitions knowing the frequency of the emitted photon.

5. Know that the Balmer series transitions are in the visible part of the spectrum.

PROCEDURE

1. Adjust the spectrometer so that the slit of the collimator is vertical. Focus the mercury light source on the collimator slit and adjust the telescope for the best image of the slit. Align the vertical cross hair with the slit. Be sure that the central notch at the center of the base of the telescope is aligned with the pencil line while making adjustments.

2. Place a sheet of paper under the telescope base and tape it firmly in place. Mark the position of the notch at the center of the base with a sharp pencil. Carefully rotate the telescope base and align the cross hair on the image of the slit for as many different spectral lines as you can find. Mark the position of the notch when you are aligned with an image of the slit. You should see two violet lines, a green line, and a yellow doublet.

3. Replace the mercury light source with the hydrogen spectrum tube and repeat the above procedure. Measure the distance from the center of rotation of the telescope base to the notch with the meter stick. Measure the distance from the central image to the first order images of the mercury lines and hydrogen lines. Using equation (1) and the values of the wavelengths of the mercury lines, calculate an average value of d, the grating spacing. The value of the sin θ is found by

$$\sin \theta = \frac{X}{R}$$

where X is the perpendicular distance from the central image to the spectral line image in question and R is the radius of curvature.

The more prominent mercury spectral lines are:

404.7 nm, violet
435.8 nm for blue-violet;
546.1 nm for green
577 nm and 579.1nm for yellow

4. Calculate the wavelengths for the hydrogen spectral lines. Determine your errors and percent errors.

5. Calculate the value for Planck's constant. Determine your errors and percent errors.

6. Calculate the number of lines per cm for your grating.

7. Using your value of Plank's constant, calculate the Rydberg constant.

QUESTIONS

1. In transitions to n = 2 photons of visible light are emitted. What light is emitted in the transition to n = 1 and n = 3?

2. Would a wavelength of 950 nm result from a transition to n= 2? Why or why not?

3. What is an empirical equation?

The Spectrum of Hydrogen and Planck's Constant

Name: _____   Date: _____

Spectral line identified by color and source Mercury	Distance from the central axis x	Radius of Curvature R	$\sin\theta = \dfrac{x}{R}$	Calculated wavelength λ nm

Spectral line identified by color and source Hydrogen	Distance from the central axis x	Radius of Curvature R	$\sin\theta = \dfrac{x}{R}$	Calculated wavelength λ nm

Open-Ended Experiments

Using only the specified equipment given for the proposed problem, design and conduct an experiment to answer the question. For each investigation, you will:

1. Do research where needed.

2. State your objective and procedure.

3. Design and make a data table if applicable.

4. Support your experiment with graphs, calculations, or observations and error analysis where applicable.

5. Draw a set of conclusions.

EXPERIMENTAL PURPOSE AND APPARATUS

OPEN-ENDED EXPERIMENT 1

Given an air track, photogate, timer and known gliders, design and conduct an experiment to determine the relationship between mass and acceleration if force is constant.

OPEN-ENDED EXPERIMENT 2

Given a meterstick, mass holder, slotted masses, and elastic bands, design and conduct an experiment to see if the elastic band obeys Hooke's Law.

OPEN-ENDED EXPERIMENT 3

Given a meterstick, scale, stopwatch and a long flight of stairs, design and conduct an experiment to determine your power output in horsepower units,

OPEN-ENDED EXPERIMENT 4

Given a meterstick, steel ball, marble, and a "live" tennis ball, design an experiment to determine the fractional change in the kinetic energy between bounces. (Hint: Research coefficient of restitution.)

OPEN-ENDED EXPERIMENT 5

Given a spring scale, a centimeter ruler, a cylindrical mass, a 1000-ml beaker and a liquid, design and conduct an experiment to determine the density of the liquid.

OPEN-ENDED EXPERIMENT 6

Given a meterstick, a pivot stand, meterstick clamps, mass hangers, and slotted masses, design and conduct an experiment to determine the mass of an unknown object and locate the center of mass of the system.

OPEN-ENDED EXPERIMENT 7

Given a meterstick, pivot stand, meterstick clamp, and a known mass, design and conduct an experiment to determine the mass of the meter stick.

OPEN-ENDED EXPERIMENT 8

Given an air table, meterstick, board protractor, and pucks of known mass, design and conduct an experiment to measure the scatter angles after a collision.

OPEN-ENDED EXPERIMENT 9

Given a Mylar balloon, inflated with helium, a string, and paper clips, design and conduct an experiment to determine the amount of gas in the balloon.

OPEN-ENDED EXPERIMENT 10

Given a balance, masses, thermometer, body of known material, Styrofoam cup, and a liquid, design and conduct an experiment to measure the specific heat of the liquid.

OPEN-ENDED EXPERIMENT 11

Given three identical containers, three thermometers, and water in the following ranges—85°C to 90°C, 50°C to 60°C, and 30°C to 35°C, design and conduct an experiment to determine the rate of cooling of a liquid. In specific terms which cools faster?

OPEN-ENDED EXPERIMENT 12

Given a ripple tank, frequency generator, light source, water, and various barriers, design and conduct an experiment to observe diffraction and interference of water waves.

OPEN-ENDED EXPERIMENT 13

Given a meterstick, concave mirror, mirror holder, screen, and object, design and conduct an experiment to determine the focal length of the mirror.

OPEN-ENDED EXPERIMENT 14

Given various 0.5 watt commercial color coded resistors, battery, switch, ammeter, voltmeter, connecting wires, and the resistance color code in the appendix, design and conduct an experiment to determine the resistance of the resistor, specifically in each case answering the following questions? Are you within the tolerance for the resistor? Does heat build up effect the outcome?(Experiment by keeping the circuit closed for short periods to see if there is a temperature factor.)

OPEN-ENDED EXPERIMENT 15

Given a compass, iron filings, glass plate, bar and horseshoe magnets, design and conduct an experiment to determine the magnetic field around the magnet.

OPEN-ENDED EXPERIMENT 16

Given coils of wire, a bar magnet, and a galvanometer determine what relationships must exist between the magnetic field and a coil of wire in order to induce a current in the galvanometer.

Appendix Tables

TABLE 1 — THE GREEK ALPHABET

Greek Letter		Greek Name	Greek Letter		Greek Name
A	α	alpha	N	ν	nu
B	β	beta	Ξ	ξ	xi
Γ	γ	gamma	O	o	omicron
Δ	δ	delta	Π	π	pi
E	ε	epsilon	P	ρ	rho
Z	ζ	zeta	Σ	σ	sigma
H	η	eta	T	τ	tau
Θ	θ	theta	Υ	υ	upsilon
I	ι	iota	Φ	ϕ	phi
K	κ	kalpa	X	χ	chi
Λ	λ	lambda	Ψ	ψ	psi
M	μ	mu	Ω	ω	omega

Source: Zober and Zober

TABLE 2 — SCIENTIFIC PREFIXES

prefix	symbol	pronunciation	exponent	magnitude
yotta-	Y	yot'ah	10^{24}	septillion
zetta-	Z	zet'ah	10^{21}	sextillion
eka-	E	ex'ah	10^{18}	quintillion
penta-	P	pe'ta	10^{15}	quadrillion
terra-	T	ter'ah	10^{12}	trillion
giga-	G	jig'ah	10^{9}	billion
mega-	M	meg'ah	10^{6}	million
kilo-	k	kil'oe	10^{3}	thousand
hecto-	h	hek'toe*	10^{2}	hundred
deka-	da	dek'ah*	10^{1}	ten
unit			10^{0}	one
deci-	d	des'i	10^{-1}	one-tenth
centi-	c	sen'ti	10^{-2}	one-hundredth
milli-	m	mil'I	10^{-3}	one-thousandth
micro-	u	my'kroe	10^{-6}	one-millionth
nano-	n	nan'oe	10^{-9}	one-billionth
pico-	p	pee'koe	10^{-12}	one-trillionth
femto-	f	fem'toe	10^{-15}	one-quadrillionth
atto-	a	at'toe	10^{-18}	one-qunitillionth
zepto-	z	zep'toe	10^{-21}	one-sextillionth
yocto	y	yoc'toe	10^{-24}	one-septillionth

The prefixes hecto- and deka- are not used in physics.

TABLE 3 — PHYSICAL CONSTANTS

Speed of Light	c	$3.00 \times 10^8 \, \frac{m}{s}$
Gravitational Constant	G	$6.67 \times 10^{-11} \, \frac{N \cdot m^2}{kg^2}$
Avogadro's Number	N_A	$6.02 \times 10^{23} \, \frac{particles}{mol}$
Gas Constant	R	$8.31 \, \frac{J}{mol \cdot K}$
Boltzmann Constant	k	$1.38 \times 10^{-23} \, \frac{J}{K}$
Coulomb Constant	$k = \dfrac{1}{4\pi\varepsilon_o}$	$9.00 \times 10^9 \, \frac{N \cdot m^2}{C^2}$
Permittivity Constant	ε_o	$8.85 \times 10^{-12} \, \frac{C^2}{N \cdot m^2}$
Permeability Constant	μ_o	$1.26 \times 10^{-6} \, \frac{T \cdot m}{A}$
Elementary Charge	e	$1.60 \times 10^{-19} \, C$
Rydeberg Constant	R	$0.01097 \, \frac{1}{nm}$

TABLE 4 — COMMON CONVERSION FACTORS

Units of English Length

Basic unit is the foot (ft)

1 ft = 12 in

1 fathom = 6 ft = 2 yd

1 yd = 3 ft = 36 in

1 mi = 5280 ft = 1760 yd

1 rod = 16.5 ft = 5.5 yd

1 chain = 66 ft = 22 yd = 4 rods

1 chain = 0.1 furlong

1 furlong = 660 ft = 220 yd

1 furlong = 40 rods

1 furlong = 0.125 mi

Units of English Weight

Basic unit is the pound (lb)

1 lb = 16 oz

1 ton = 2000 lb

1 lb = 7000 grain

Units of SI Length

Unit is the meter (m)

1 m = 100 cm = 1000 mm

1 cm = 10

1 km = 1000 m

The micron (μ):

$1 \mu = 1 \times 10^{-6}$ m = 1 μm

The millimicron (mμ):

$1 m\mu = 1 \times 10^{-9}$ m

The angstrom (Å):

$1 Å = 1 \times 10^{-10}$ m

The fermi:

$1 \text{ fermi} = 1 \times 10^{-15}$ m = 1 fm

Units of English Volume

Basic unit is the cubic foot (ft^3)

$1 \text{ ft}^3 = 1728 \text{ in}^3$

$1 \text{ yd}^3 = 27 \text{ ft}^3$

1 gal = 4 qt

1 qt = 2 pt

$1 \text{ gal} = 231 \text{ in}^3$

$1 \text{ ft}^3 = 7.480$ gal

1 qt = 4 cups

1 cup = 48 teaspoons (tsp)

1 tablespoon (tbsp) = 3 tsp

Common Units of Time

The unit of time is the second (s)

1 hr = 60 min = 3600 s

1 d = 24 hr

1 d = 86400 s

$1 \text{ yr} = 365.242 \text{ d} = 3.156 \times 10^7$ s

Units of SI Volume

Unit is the cubic meter (m^3)

$1 \text{ m}^3 = 1 \times 10^6 \text{ cm}^3$

$1 \text{ m}^3 = 1000 \text{ L} = 1 \times 10^6$ mL

1 L = 1000 mL

1 L = 1000 cc

$1 \text{ L m}^3 = 1 \text{ mL} = 1$ cc

Units of SI Mass

Unit is the kilogram (kg)

1 kg = 1000 g

1 g = 1000 mg

The metric tonne (MT):

1 MT = 1000 kg

$1 \text{ u} = 1.660 \times 10^{-27}$ kg

English-SI Length Factors

1 in = 2.540 cm

1 cm = 0.394 in

1 ft = 30.48 cm

1 m = 3.281 ft

1 m = 39.370 in

1 mi = 1.609 km

1 km = 0.621 mi

1 rod = 5.029 m

English-SI Volume Factors

1 ft^3 = 28.317 L

1 in^3 = 16.387 cm^3

1 L = 1.057 qt

1 m^3 = 35.315 ft^3

1 qt = 0.946 L

1 qt = 946 cm^3

1 L = 61.0 in^3

1 gal = 3.785 L

English-SI Mass and Weight Factors

1 lb = 453.592 g

1 kg = 2.205 lb

1 oz = 28.349 g

1 mg = 0.015 grain

1 MT = 1.102 tons

TABLE 5 — MASS DENSITY

At 1 atmosphere of pressure and at 0°C.

Material	$\rho\left(\dfrac{kg}{m^3}\right)$	$\rho\left(\dfrac{g}{cm^3}\right)$	specific gravity
air	1.29	1.29×10^{-3}	
aluminum, Al	2.70×10^3	2.70	2.7
benzene, C_6H_6	0.879×10^3	0.879	0.879
brass	8.70×10^3	8.70	8.70
cadmium, Cd	8.38×10^3	8.38	8.38
copper, Cu	8.92×10^3	8.92	8.92
ethyl alcohol, C_2H_5OH	0.806×10^3	0.806	0.806
common glass	2.60×10^3	2.60	2.60
glycerin, $C_3H_5(OH)_3$	1.26×10^3	1.26	1.26
gold, Au	19.3×10^3	19.3	19.3
ice	0.917×10^3	0.917	0.917
iron, Fe	7.86×10^3	7.86	7.86
lead, Pb	11.3×10^3	11.3	11.3
mercury, Hg	13.6×10^3	13.6	13.6
nickel, Ni	8.68×10^3	8.68	8.68
oak (seasoned)	0.713×10^3	0.713	0.713
pine (seasoned)	0.378×10^3	0.378	0.378
platinum, Pt	21.4×10^3	21.4	21.4
seawater	1.03×10^3	1.03	1.03
silver, Ag	10.5×10^3	10.5	10.5
tin, Sn	7.29×10^3	7.29	7.29
water (@2.98°C)	1.00×10^3	1.00	1.00

TABLE 6 — RESISTOR COLOR CODES

Color	Number	Multiplier	Tolerance
Black	0	1	
Brown	1	10	
Red	2	10^2	
Orange	3	10^3	
Yellow	4	10^4	
Green	5	10^5	
Blue	6	10^6	
Violet	7	10^7	
Gray	8	10^8	
White	9	10^9	
Gold			5%
Silver			10%
No Color			20%

TABLE 7 — AMERICAN WIRE GAUGE FOR COPPER AT 20°C

Gauge Number	Diameter mm	Gauge Number	Diameter mm
0000	11.68	19	0.9116
000	10.40	20	0.8118
00	9.266	21	0.7230
0	8.252	22	0.6438
1	7.348	23	0.5733
2	6.544	24	0.5106
3	5.827	25	0.4547
4	5.189	26	0.4049
5	4.621	27	0.3606
6	4.115	28	0.3211
7	3.665	29	0.2859
8	3.264	30	0.2546
9	2.906	31	0.2268
10	2.588	32	0.2019
11	2.305	33	0.1798
12	2.053	34	0.1606
13	1.828	35	0.1426
14	1.628	36	0.1270
15	1.450	37	0.1131
16	1.291	38	0.1007
17	1.150	39	0.08969
18	1.024	40	0.07987

TABLE 8 — COMMON RESISTIVITIES AT 20°C

Material	Resistivity ($\times 10^{-8}$ Ω m)
Aluminum	2.65
Brass (Cu 70.2%, Zn 29.8%)	7.85
Climax	87
Constantan (Cu 60%, Ni 40%)	49
Copper	1.72
German silver (Cu 55%, Zn 25%, Ni 20%)	33.3
Gold	2.44
Iron	10.1
Manganin (Cu 82%, Mn 15%, Ni 3%)	44.1
Mercury	95.8
Monel metal (Ni 60%, Cu 33%, Fe 7%)	42.0
Nichrome (Ni 60%, Fe 24%, Cr 16%)	100
Nickel	6.84
Nickel silver (Cu 57%, Ni 43%)	48.8
Silver	1.63
Tungsten	5.51

TABLE 9 — INDEX OF REFRACTION

$\lambda = 589$ nm @ 20°

Air, dry (S.T.P.)	1.00029
Alcohol, ethyl (C_2H_5OH)	1.360
Benzene (C_6H_6)	1.501
Canada balsam	1.530
Carbon dioxide (S.T.P.)	1.00045
Carbon disulfide (CS_2)	1.625
Carbon tetrachloride (CCl_4)	1.459
Diamond	2.417
Glass, crown	1.517
flint	1.575
dense flint	1.66
Glycerol ($C_3H_4(OH)_3$)	1.475
Ice	1.31
Lucite	1.51
Quartz, fused (SiO_2)	1.45845
Sodium chloride (NaCl)	1.544
Vacuum	1.0000
Water, distilled	1.333
Water vapor (S.T.P.)	1.00025